Spring Creek Chronicles II

*More stories of Commercial Fishin', huntin', workin'
and people along the Gulf Coast*

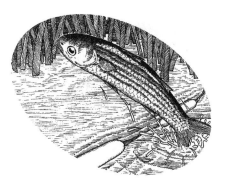

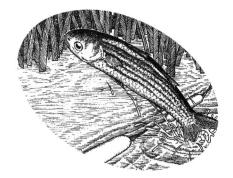

Spring Creek Chronicles II

*More stories of Commercial Fishin', huntin', workin'
and people along the Gulf Coast*

Written by Leo Lovel

Illustrated by Clay Lovel

Edited by Ben Lovel

Leo V. Lovel
Tallahassee, Florida

ISBN 0-97096-1626

Leo V. Lovel
Spring Creek Restaurant
33 Ben Willis Road
Crawfordville, Florida 32327
(850) 926-3751

Introduction

Spring Creek Chronicles II is fifty or so more short stories written along the same lines as the stories contained in the original Spring Creek Chronicles.

Again these are a collection of observations, opinions, true-life experiences and related tales gathered from living and working on the Gulf Coast and in the woods of the Deep South.

The community of Spring Creek is a small commercial fishing village located at the end of County Road 365 that deadends into the Gulf of Mexico. Two fish houses, one church, forty or fifty residents and Spring Creek Restaurant make up the town. Commercial fishing, crabbing and oystering have been the backbone of the economy forever. The freshwater springs here pump 1294 million gallons of water a day and dump it directly into the gulf. Saltwater fish, freshwater fish, oysters, shrimp, crabs, alligators, otters, ducks, birds of every kind abound in the bay. Deer, turkey, bear, hogs and all the woods animals there are, live along the shoreline.

These stories give an insight into the habits of most of these creatures and some of the people of the area too. I'll never be able to put into words the excitement, the fear, the beauty, the wonder and the craziness of it all.

Enjoy these stories, cause we sure enjoyed livin' em.

This poem was written by my grandfather just a few months before his sudden, accidental, tragic death.
I never met him but I feel like I know him.

Be happy and gay
Don't ever be sad
Think what awaits you
Not what you've had

The skies can't be blue
Every day that's true
But always on the morrow
The sun shines thru

So as thru life
We struggle and strive
Isn't it a pleasure
To just be alive?

Leo Holden Lovel
December 1942
March 29, 1905 - September 1, 1943

Contents

WAYWARD BIRD

CLAY MARSHALL LOVEL
04

Wayward Bird

We'd had two full days of a hard Southwest wind, blowing a steady twenty knots, churning the clear waters of the Gulf to something like weak chocolate milk.

We're happily tied to the dock, knowing we'd just baited-up our Stone Crab traps the day before the weather broke out and we're just waiting for the wind to switch around, knowing our traps are filling up with crabs cause this is the kind of blow the crabs move heavy in, come out of their hiding places to feed in, or to migrate offshore to warmer areas.

The wind turns around to blow a hard Northeaster around midnight and we're fueled, bait loaded and heading out at daylite to gather in that load of Stone Crab claws.

And let me tell you it's kicking-it five miles offshore in this grey, drizzly Northeaster, the only color besides grey is white, the color of the wave-tops as they are being blown-off the seven-foot seas that are breaking over the bow of the ACE as we turn straight into the wind and the falling tide to hook the buoys on our traps.

The wind is howling thru the rigging, spray like a hard sideways rain blowing across the side and rolling around our feet and out the scuppers.

I'm pulling the traps, hooking the buoys with my gaff sometimes at eye level because of the wave height, sometimes I'm bending over the side of the boat to reach 'em cause they're down at the bottom of the swell.

Ben's shaking out the crabs, stuffing fish heads in the bait well and throwing the traps back in the water as I'm hooking the next trap.

Jake is guiding the boat down the trap line, cussing at the difficulty he's having spotting the next trap and trying to keep steerage in the breaking seas, standing at the wheel instead of sitting in the captain's chair cause he can't turn the steering wheel fast enough sitting down.

It's bad-time rough.

We're catching big-time crabs, caught up in the haul.

Keeping balance and focus is a full time job.

Ben jabs me on the arm and says, "Look at that, Dad," pointing out beyond the stern of the boat.

Flying at full speed, wings at the RPM of a humming bird, is some kind of little bird, trying to fly against the twenty knot Nor'easter to gain the sanctuary of the boat.

The bird is not gaining ground against the wind, and is barely maintaining enough height to clear the foaming waves rolling past the stern of the boat.

We pull a trap or two glancing back at the life or death struggle of the wayward bird.

He's losing distance and he's losing height from the swells.

I yell at Jake to slow the boat down so the bird can catch up.

Jake yells back that he can't slow down or he will lose steerage against the pounding seas and we'll take one over the side.

A sensible and reasonable decision so I don't say anymore and concentrate on trying to keep up with the pulling of the traps. It's so rough that if we miss one we just go on to the next one, not wanting to go back and turn sideways to the seas, but we hate missing one cause they are loaded with crabs.

The bird is still trying to catch us but he's falling behind.

And he's slowly losing altitude, barely staying above the whitecaps and the flying foam.

Ben and I are both watching as an extra big swell rolls out from behind the boat and breaks into a white foaming curl and slaps that hard-flying bird down into the water, folding him into the hard-grey sea like egg whites into the dough. Mixed-up and lost forever.

Ben and I both felt bad, for we knew he was a land

bird, and the sea had claimed 'em for good.

Not much time was spent worrying about the fate of that little bird cause the trap- pulling never missed a beat, and the working conditions were challenging enough to keep your mind focused on staying on your feet and staying in the boat.

Ten minutes later we're a crab catching machine, fighting rough water, pulling and dumping traps, pouring ten to twenty big crabs a trap into boxes, a good payday coming.

Then we notice the bird again.

Same as before, flapping his wings like a bee to gain the boat but he can't gain on us against the wind.

Ben and I both yell at Jake again to slow down but at the same time the bird's slapped out of the air like a fly-with-a swatter by another big wave.

The bird is back in the air in seconds, taking flight from out of the water like a duck. I never knew land birds could take-off outta the water.

This time Ben and I yell at Jake hard enough and he backs off the throttle, complaining, cussing, fighting that steering wheel.

And the bird's catching up to us, slow but sure, taking a full minute to fly forty feet to the boat against the wind and spray.

Just as he's about to reach us he's knocked down again into the churning seas at the same time the ACE is slammed on the port quarter by a big swell and we're pushed sideways, rolling hard to starboard where Ben and I are standing.

And the little bird is swirling by, rolling through the water in a wave-top, the ACE and the bird both under the total control of the seas and only five feet apart but too far for me to reach 'em.

But not too far for Ben.

Like some kind of action hero in a maelstrom of roaring white capped waves with spray flying in sheets across the deck of a pitching, rolling bucking boat, Ben, slicker suit clad, hood cinched down tight, heavy coat and boots grabs the support strut with his left hand and swings his whole body over the rail and grabs the little bird with his right hand.

As fine a catch as I've ever seen in any sport, executed with the most perfect timing and agility under the most difficult conditions.

Dangerous, dangerous, dangerous.

Literally risking your life for a little bird.

A Field Lark as it turns out, a wet, tired but lucky Field Lark.

And Ben set 'em on the edge of the bait boxes where he blinked and fluffed a few times then hopped down to the deck and hopped, hopped, hopped up to the cabin and made his way to the bunks like an invited guest, once on the bunks he hopped his way to the furthest point in the bow, the driest darkest place, and went to sleep.

And we went back to work and had a whale of a catch of claws, forgetting about the bird for a few hours.

We're steaming up the Spring Creek Channel, the sky has cleared, the wind has laid and switched more west, it's a beautiful day, a different world from the weather of the morning.

The claws are broke, the boat's washed clean, we're relaxing, looking at the green pines and oaks growing in a solid mass on the shore line only a half-mile off.

We notice Field Lark has perched himself on the starboard window sill, looking at that shoreline too.

He stared for a minute or so, flutters down to the deck. Bird-hops his way between the three of us, paying us no mind like he had known us forever. When he reaches the open deck he flutters his way up to the rail and sits there, watching that shoreline, fluffing his wings and feathers.

And without so much as a chirp or a thank-you Field

4

Lark jumps up off the rail and flies straight as an arrow toward those beautiful trees.

Wonder what a Field Lark was doing so far out in the Gulf anyway.

I bet it will be hard to get him to go offshore fishing again.

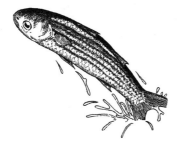

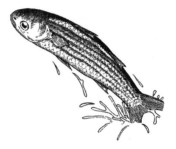

Summer Thunder Showers

I can recall vividly, wading around the edge of Lake Jackson in the summertime, dangling a hand-dug worm on a cane pole for bream, watching the sky get dark in mid-afternoon, knowing that a big thunder squall was coming not only by the black clouds but by the rumble of thunder in the distance getting closer and closer.

The though of getting wet didn't bother me much cause the house wasn't five hundred yards away, but the possibility of some excitement and a good foot-race interested me if the rainstorm made up like I hoped it would.

Our summer afternoon rains seemed as regular as the six o'clock news when I was coming up. I think it rained most every afternoon. If you were lined-up in the right place you could pit yourself against Mother Nature for a minute or two and see who was faster.

You could see, smell, feel and hear, especially hear, that deluge coming, particularly if you were at the edge of the big lake and the rain was coming across it.

The air got a fresh scent to it.

You could see a solid grey wall marching across the lake blotting out all sight beyond it.

The coolness being pushed ahead of that wall of water was a God-given treat to a sweaty boy in July.

But the noise of it coming was the most impressive to me, the sound of a mile-wide waterfall beating the water of Lake Jackson flat, a low roar getting louder and louder as it got closer.

And I'd get ready for the race.

Laying down my fishing pole and turning my back to the storm, placing one foot ahead of the other like a sprinter on the track, looking back over my shoulder at the competition, wanting it to get near enough to give ole Mom Nature a chance to drench me if she could but I wanted to be fair.

The big giant drops of rain that seem to fall a few hundred yards ahead of the solid wall of water didn't count.

Those were just to scare you and make you run too soon.

I could usually stand it until that racing sheet of water was just a good baseball throw behind me, unless a bolt of lightning or the crack of thunder made me bolt too soon out of fright.

But under normal circumstances I'd wait until the indescribable crash and roar of the pouring rain would tell me it was time to go; then I'd go like a scared rabbit.

And in those days this little barefoot boy could fly on his feet, not needing to glance back to see if I was winning, that locomotive sound that was getting louder and louder told me all I needed to know.

Sometimes I won and sometimes I lost, running full blast into the carport, barely being able to slow down before I hit the back wall of the kitchen.

Sometimes dry, sometimes so wet I might as well have been swimming, but always exhilarated, panting for breath, watching the water pour in sheets off the roof and listen to it beating on the shingles like a drum.

Win or lose I was happy, sheltered, only punished if I lost by being pelted by that icy water from the sky and only disappointed if I had started running too soon and had to wait a minute or so before the rain got there.

Those were simple times.

Good times.

Times when kids could amuse themselves with a cane pole and a rainstorm or a mud puddle or a Sears catalog and a pen, blacking out teeth and drawing mustaches.

Times I wish we could go back to.

But I know I couldn't.

I'd have to start running now as soon as I saw the sky start getting clouded up.

My 1st Mullet

My first mullet is not a story about the first mullet I
ever caught but about the first mullet I ever ate.

I was in Boy Scouts, Troop 115 based out of St. Paul's
Methodist Church in Tallahassee.

I was brand-new to the troop and the first function
was a campout somewhere in the Apalachicola National
Forest.

Nobody picked me for a tent-mate cause nobody
knew me and I didn't know anybody either.

We got out in the woods, pitched our pup-tents, got
everything ready for the nite as best we could. I put up
my tent alone, with the help of one of the Scoutmasters
and joined the rest of the Scouts around the fire to roast
hotdogs on green limbs, eating 'em with mustard and
ketchup, some tater-chips and cokes.

Soon as it got black-dark we were all instructed to go
to our tents, get in our beds and go to sleep, which we all
answered with a bunch of "yes sirs" that was expected
and demanded of boys raised in the early 60's.

No arguments or whining.

I didn't have far to go cause my tent was pitched
close to the big campfire where the Scoutmasters camped.
I guess cause I was the only one camping alone and the
grown-ups thought I'd probably be scared.

I crawl in my sleeping bag, jeans, socks and all, not
sleepy, plenty excited and wonderous.

I can hear the Scoutmasters talkin low, firing up a gas
fryer, mixing drinks, chuckling, preparing to cook
something.

I can hear fish sizzling when it's dropped in the
boiling lard.

I can smell the fish frying, drifting on the cool fall air,
filling my nose and head with flavor, making my mouth
water, making me so bold as to put my shoes back on and

slip out of the tent to crawl and spy-on what was going on.

There they are.

Set-up by the side of the campfire with an old Coleman stove going. A black-iron skillet full of melted lard, they are picking pieces of crispy fish out of the pan laying 'em on a clean board.

My eyes are watering those fish smelled so good. That fresh-ground coarse cornmeal, fried golden brown with liberal amounts of salt and pepper smelled like popcorn at the movies with an extra-special fish scent thrown in.

Like only fried mullet in the woods can smell on a cool fall nite.

I edge a little closer and step on a dry limb and break it with a loud "crack".

The fish-cookers look around and see me hiding behind a tree.

"Come here boy," one of 'em orders me, not mean sounding but demanding.

"What ya doin' out there?" he says as I slowly walk into the fire lite, sorta embarrassed and scared.

"I couldn't help but come see what was going on when I smelled that cooking smell and heard that fryin' sound," I replied, not knowin' if I was in trouble or not.

"Want something to eat?" one of 'em says as he puts a half-a-piece of crisp, hot fried mullet on one slice of white-bread and hands it to me.

I've got to be respectful and take it and mumble "thank-you, sir," as I feel the heat from the fried fish thru the bread.

"Go on back to bed now, boy," I'm instructed as I duck back in my pup-tent.

I peel me a strip of that hot fish off the skin, close to the rib cage and pop it in my mouth.

Good gracious alive!

This tastes like something only angels could get to eat.

The salt, the meal, the grease, the fish, the greasy bread are the best thing I've every tasted, blended with the cool air, the lighter-wood smell from the fire, the night sounds, the outdoors primitive feel.

I've caught, cleansed and cooked a million pounds of mullet since then but I've never forgotten the first one.

10 A.M. to 10 P.M.

10 A.M.

Slick calm, low-low tide, bright sunshine, plenty cool enough for a jacket but not enough for gloves.

The airboat's skimming along, about forty. You know where you're going and you can count on fish being where you think they are — at least you think you can, or they should be, they need to be, they can't be anywhere else —?

But they're there today.

Not showing much sign, but enough sign to dump the skimpy one hundred and sixty-feet of net in a tiny circle and watch fish begin to jump like popcorn, like grasshoppers along the perimeter of the net and in the wake of the airboat as I spin it in a tight circle around the outside of the net and in the center of the circle.

Blue, blue sky, calm slick water.

Bright sunshine, no wind the most passive place in the universe. Have to shed the jacket. It's so warm and pretty.

10 P.M.

I'm standing on the dock, checking the lines on the boats.

It's raining, the wind's blowing twenty-five knots, palm fronds rattling, pine needles whistling everything is wet.

No stars in the sky.

Then you see a star.

And then another one and then two or three more stars then they're gone.

The wind lays down for two seconds then picks-up and increases, going from southwest to more westerly and puffs, (increasing then decreasing) and puffs again, then gains strength pulling more around to the north and north-west.

More stars appear.

Then constellations, and the sky is more clear than clouded.

And the temperature begins to fall and the air drys out, and the tide starts to blast-out from the wind and the moon.

And you know what you can do again in those same holes in those same creeks and you say "Thanks" again for standing on the dock watching the weather "kickin' it", rather than being out in the weather and being kicked by it.

Twelve hours.

Half-a-day.

Such a small amount of time when you think about it and such a wide variety of weather and conditions and challenges and emotions and comforts and discomforts, defeats and victories.

A lot can happen in twelve hours.

October 20, 1997

We untied the airboat from the dock that morning. Pushed her out in the canal and fired her up, idling our way toward the mouth of Spring Creek, going through our normal routine in preparation for a morning of mullet fishing.

We'd been doing pretty good for the last couple of weeks. Fishing everyday that the State of Florida allowed us to, which was only Monday thru Friday at noon. We were scraping up two to six hundred pounds of fish pretty regular. Giving us all we needed for the restaurant and plenty of extra to sell on the fresh market. The fish were bringing a good price cause they were starting to have red-roe in 'em.

Today's fishing was going to be different.

More stress and strain involved, and you could already tell it and see it in the way Ben and I went through our duties.

Ben's checking the conditions of the nets, straightening up the lead line, checking the knots where the net-ropes are tied together, making sure the staff-rope is clear.

I'm checking the gauges, the oil pressure, temperature, amps, physically looking over the engine for oil or coolant leaks. We're going a long ways from here, in shallow water that can be treacherous, unreachable places in conventional boats. We want everything working just right.

Usually we've got a banter going when we're idling out and working, cutting the fool with each other, excited about the day ahead, commenting on how pretty the day is.

But not this morning. Cause we had both read in the local paper, The Wakulla News, that the Florida Marine Patrol had launched a task force, to stop all the illegal net fishing for mullet.

Beginning October 20th.

I had decided that we might as well keep on fishing like we had been everyday. That if we stopped today, we wouldn't go tomorrow, or the next day or the next. The task force was here for the duration of Run Season and that's when we needed to fish the most.

If we stop today then we might as well stop for good.

We were used to the planes, the undercover boats, the night-surveillance, the ambushes and traps. We hated that helicopter the worst cause you couldn't elude 'em or get away from 'em but we had learned to live with that too.

The way the laws were written and interpreted was crazy.

The nets we had on the boat were legal to possess.

It was legal to put 'em in the water.

It was legal to fish two nets at the same time.

It was legal to possess fish on the boat.

But it was illegal to be caught with fish in the net, or to have the two nets tied together, but the net ropes being tied together was still an unresolved question in the Florida District Court of Appeals.

We'll just have to be more on our toes, more alert, make sure we're cleared up and untied before we get checked.

The enjoyment is going out of this line of work.

The boat's warmed up, the gear is ready, it's time to let the horses run on that 300hp GM motor, and start running and searching the shore-line for fish.

The tide is right, the wind is light and the fish are looking good. We've struck four times from Spring Creek to the head of Goose Creek Bay and have well over three hundred pounds. If it was before the net-ban and we had our monofilament nets we'd have three thousand pounds, but at least we're still fishing.

I can tell it's about dead-low tide, and the fish ought

to be bunched-up-right on the mud flats between Big Pass and Little Pass. A hard to get to area on the west side of the St. Marks River, one of our low-tide honey holes.

We haven't seen a surveillance plane, the helicopter or even a patrol boat and you can bet we've been looking.

I'm scoping things out good as we run into Little Pass, sliding across mud and grass flats that are fully uncovered by the low tide. My focus goes over to fish as we run by a marsh grass island that separates Big Pass from Little Pass and there's a big mud basin that holds about a foot of water and tons of mullet on most low tides.

The fish are there and they're making a break for the center of the basin. All my attention is on trying to make a circle with that little piece of net they let us have, trying to pen-up a couple of hundred head of mullet so we can catch a few.

We manage to get that net around a good pod of mullet and they're taking to the net pretty good, shaking the corkline when they hit it, a big portion of the mullet using their heads and just jumping over the net and swimming away free.

I've got the airboat back to a slow idle from that wild slide we'd had it in making that tiny circle.

Ben is standing on the front net deck, waiting for me to idle up to the cork that marks the end of the net so we can start bolting it back on the boat, taking the fish out.

Ben reaches down and grabs the cork. I shut the boat off and remove the ear-muffs we wear to protect our ears from the high pitch whine the propeller makes.

I'm swinging down from the driver's platform to help clear the fish when we both jerk out heads around at a new sound, to see a new sight that we hadn't seen before and now wish we'd never seen.

It's a light tan airboat that's in a side-ways slide going seventy miles an hour. That boat is breaking around the end of the marsh grass island we had just passed, headed for us like a rocket.

And we both immediately know who it is and what they're up to.

And our legal nets are placed legally in the water but there is no way to get the fish cleared out of 'em in the two seconds before that boat gets here.

It's time to do something quick.

I tell Ben to drop the end of the net he's holding and I fly back up into the driver's seat. I fire up those three hundred and thirty horses, spin the boat around 180 degrees, stomp on the gas pedal and blast up and over an oyster bar that's right behind us and shut the boat back down. We glide to a stop on the mud, a hundred yards from out net.

The brand-new FMP airboat is trying to come back under control, sliding by us at a hundred miles an hour, over-shooting us by two hundred yards. He's going so fast in his eagerness to apprehend us with fish in the net, but he's under control now, (or at least his boat is), sliding up to us and grabbling on to our boat.

It's Florida Mullet Police officer Bubba and he's talking real excited into his fancy two-way radio that's built into some kind of crash-helmet he's wearing on his head. He's convicting us over the airways to his superior officers, telling 'em we've got a mile of monofilament gill net struck off and a load of fish in it.

Ole Bubba is "yes sirring" this and "yes sirring" that over his fancy headset, getting his final instructions, he hasn't said a word to us yet but he's fixing to.

He snatches off his headset, jumps over to our boat, points his finger in my face and snarls, "Go get that net."

He's in an unmarked boat, he ain't wearing no uniform, he's got a badge and a gun strapped to his belt so there's no doubt who he is, but he is very rude and disrespectful.

He hasn't asked who we are, what we're doing, he hasn't even properly introduced himself and yet he's giving us orders like we are a couple of school children and he's the principal.

I answer his crudely put demand with a one word answer.

"No," is my response.

"You go get that net," he yells pointing at the net and pointing at us with that same rude finger.

"I'm not gonna do it," I say again.

"You go get that net right now or I'm taking both of you to jail," he's threatening. He's mad now, not used to being disobeyed.

I can tell you, this guy ain't got no manners at all.

I'm getting upset now, and I tell him, "You ain't taking us anywhere, and if you want that net so bad, you go get it yourself."

That truly upset ole Bubba.

His eyes bugged out, he had foam on his lips, his mouth was moving but he wasn't saying any words. He didn't know what to do, so he did what he always did, he crammed back on that fancy headset and called for more instructions from the task force commander.

After a long conversation, which we can hear only one side of, he removes his fancy talking device and asks that we give him our fishing licenses.

He looks them over, sticks both licenses in his pocket and tells us to follow him over to the nets.

Officer Bubba seems to have calmed down some as he cranks up his boat and idles it around the oyster bar, easing his boat up to that round circle of corkline where you can see quite a few mullet tails flipping and flapping, stuck in the net, waiting for somebody to get 'em out and ice 'em down in a fish box.

Me and Ben are in no hurry.

We already know that whatever happens with the rest of this day, it's not going to be good. We've been laid for, targeted and caught. No matter that the legal methods of fishing are still being debated, we are guilty until we can prove ourselves innocent.

I believe that something is backwards about that.

Anyway we follow ole Bubba over to the net. Before we can get there ole Bubba is grabbing hold to the end of it, trying to rope it on his boat and Ben and I both know that he can't do it by himself.

The water is so shallow that one man has got to run the boat, cause the tide has gotten so low that the boats won't float, you've got to use the engine to drive the boat and force it over the mud, as one man on the bow ropes the net and fish on the front.

Bubba gives up and goes back on the radio to headquarters.

He chats for a minute, nodding his head from time to time, yes sirring again and again like he's talking to the President. He gets his final instructions, removes his headset and tells us we will just have to wait till the tide comes back enough to get another Marine Patrol boat in here to help 'em load the net.

Well I know it's going to be three or four hours till a conventional outboard-powered boat can come in this area, and I don't want to wait that long, so I come right out and make this offer; "I don't know whose net that is, but if you'll drive that airboat down the net, I'll get on your boat and trip the net on it for you, so we can get on with it. We don't have all day to wait."

And that's what we did.

And I had kind of a sick feeling roping that net I'd hung-in myself, with all those pretty fat mullet in it, fish we needed to cook at the restaurant, fish we needed to sell. Knowing what kind of battle we had ahead of us, knowing that this was probably the beginning of the end, that Ben was upset and mad almost to the boiling point and that I was mad at the State and mad at myself for getting my son in this mess.

Ben idles over and picks me up, getting me off that Marine Patrol boat, a boat that has now got our fish, our

22

net, our future stacked on the front of it.

Officer Bubba, conferring again with headquarters, set up at the St. Marks Lighthouse, asks us to follow him to the boat ramp located there.

And that's what we did.

Chapter Two

Things did not look good as we idled up the canal to the launch ramp at the lighthouse. There were three FMP vehicles parked where we could see 'em and a whole flock of black and grey clad officers waiting on us.

Officer Bubba nudges his airboat up on the mud beside the ramp and we slide up along side of 'em.

Lt. Robby Barfus is the task force commander and he's quizzing the arresting officer, the other officers are snapping pictures of our fish-laden net and of our boat, recording the evidence I guess.

An older gentleman, that had been fishing in the river, is loading his old aluminum boat up on his trailer next to the FMP airboat that has our net and fish piled on the bow. The fish are still flopping around in the net and the old man is looking at those fresh Red-Roe mullet while he's winching his boat up. The old man up and says, "Boy those mullet are pretty, I sure wish I had me a mess of 'em."

Lt. Barfus coldly informs the old fella that those fish are confiscated evidence and that they are now property of the State of Florida and he can't have any of 'em.

I promptly tell the man that I've got plenty of fresh mullet in my ice box and I'd be glad to give him some.

The old man's face brightens up and he reaches over and grabs a small bucket out of the back of his truck and starts heading over to our boat to get his fish.

Lt. Barfus has been listening to our conversation and as the old man approaches our airboat, Lt. Barfus jumps out in front of the old man with his arms spread wide like a basketball player defending the goal, informing the old man that he can't have any of those fish either, that they are property of the State, too.

That's when I start to argue telling Barfus that they have not seen us catch a fish, that the fish in the net may be in question but the three hundred pounds of fish in the box are mine and I can do what I want to with 'em, that the FMP has no right to these fish.

Lt. Barfus quickly calls in two officers and instructs them to read us our Miranda rights that he's going to arrest us and take us to jail for interfering with an officer.

I've no choice but to surrender the hard-caught fish in the box, cause no matter how wrong it was for the FMP to take those fish, it wasn't worth Ben and I going to jail over, a place we've never been and never intend on going.

The old man looked mighty depressed not getting his fresh mullet.

Lt. Barfus looked mighty proud and pompous.

The law held us there a good two hours, photographing, conferring up at their trucks, writing out tickets, talking to headquarters up in Tallahassee. Up to this point all the officers have been gruff and rude, demanding this, barking about that. Now they come walking down to us and they are all smiles and politeness.

We aren't smiling, we're not happy and we damn sure don't feel very polite.

Lt. Barfus has got our big yellow tickets in his hand but he's got a favor to ask before he gives 'em to us.

"Mr. Lovel," he says, grinning like some monkey that ate the last banana, "would you and your son be so kind as to clear the fish from the net for us, ya'll are so much quicker and better at it than we are, it would go a lot faster."

I can't believe it.

They've threatened to take us to jail. They're

charging us with a major violation of the Florida Constitution, confiscating all our fish and our nets, jeopardizing our livelihood and our way of life and they want us to do them a favor.

A flat out "No" is my response, we're not touching that net or those fish. They want those fish so bad they can get 'em out.

Lt. Barfus quits smiling and informs us that we'll have to wait there till the officers can get the net cleared and it will be a slow process.

I tell 'em I don't care how long it takes we ain't touching 'em.

None of the boys in the bruise colored uniforms of the FMP are happy now cause Lt. Barfus has instructed all his underlings to clear the fish out of the net.

Me and Ben break out our mustard and mayo, our light bread and ham and build us a sandwich as the FMP boys put on elbow length rubber gloves and start wrestling the fish out of the webbing.

What a silly sight they were, holding the muddy-wet net out away from their bodies, struggling to untangle the fish, trying not to drip mud and fish-juice on their shiny patent leather shoes or soil their starched ugly uniforms.

Quite a large audience had built up their at the boat ramp. There was a good crowd of good-ole-boys sitting on their tailgates, checking out the two state-of-the-art airboats, (ours and the FMP's), watching the officers try to clear the net, listening to the goings on between the law and us.

Finally the last fish is cleared out, the nets and the three hundred and sixty pounds of fish are loaded into the FMP trucks. Our tickets are handed to us and we are released to go.

Ben and I both had remained real calm during this whole affair, not shouting or yelling or cussing, but believe me, we were anything but calm inside.

25

Ben pushes the boat out from the shore and takes a push pole and shoves the bow around, pointing it down the canal.

All the FMP officers line up on the boat ramp, their patent leather toes just inches from the water's edge, looking real satisfied with themselves on the big case they had made, their Ray-Bans on, their badges shining in the sun. A smug, cocky bunch.

I could see all the good-ole-boy spectators watching us leave from the top of the ramp.

That's the last time I looked back as I climbed in the driver's seat and cranked the engine.

I idled about ten feet and then all the pent-up frustration and madness came out thru my foot and I stomped on the gas pedal, turning all 330 horses loose on that six bladed prop, roaring down the canal and out into the river.

Have you ever been behind an airboat or seen what goes on in the path of all that air that's blowing out providing the thrust that propels the boat.

It's not a place you want to be even at thirty yards, much less thirty-feet, cause it generates a good hundred mile an hour wind, blowing water, grass and mud everywhere and to be honest I wasn't even thinking about my prop wash or who was standing back there or anything else but releasing some energy and leaving this place.

I guess I should of thought about it cause I think we paid a heavy price for soaking those FMP boys down, blowing their hats into the next world and spattering-up their Ray-Bans. From that day on the Marine Patrol was with us everywhere we went.

Laying ambushes for us behind anchored sailboats and in the marsh grass.

Hovering over us with helicopters.

Circling in planes.

Stared at thru binoculars.

Followed at "discreet" distances.

Spied on and harassed to the limit.

Back to the violations we were charged with.

When we left the boat ramp at the lighthouse we each had a ticket for fishing a gill-net in state waters. When the newspaper came out two days later we found out that we had three charges against us, the original one plus fishing a net over 500 square feet and resisting arrest. That was a heck of a way to be notified.

I was relieved about one thing that was printed in the paper, about us being charged and all, and that was that they printed the official weight of the fish we had caught that day and it was over 300 pounds.

I would have really been embarrassed if they had given us all this press and we had been caught and charged possessing only a dozen or so fish. Three hundred pounds is a catch to be proud of with the little bit of legal gear we were fishing.

To bring this tale to an end I'll list the consequences of going fishing that late October day.

Over two years in court, finally winding up with a jury trial.

We proved our nets were legal nets.

We proved we were innocent of resisting arrest.

We were found guilty of fishing a net over 500 square feet cause we had the head ropes attached so both nets would come off the boat, our netting wasn't attached but that could not be considered according to the judge.

This charge, that we were found guilty of, is a violation of the Constitution of the State of Florida.

This was our first and only fishing violation in our twenty-five year fishing history.

Here's what it cost us.

$5000.00 in civil penalties paid to the State.

$425.00 in county fees.

$11,247.00 in attorney fees.

Forfeiture of our nets.

Forfeiture of the fish we had caught.

Forfeiture of our commercial fishing licenses for ninety days which denied us from catching our own fish and crabs for our restaurant.

$16,000.00 and change plus the loss of the value of the seafood we couldn't catch.

Pretty heavy.

That event changed our life a lot.

It pushed us into doing different things and doing things differently.

And now that I think back on that beautiful day of October 20th, I wish we had stayed on the hill, or the boat had refused to start.

Bragging Rights

We had taken the boys out on the ACE, sons and nephews, ages 12 to 16, for a hopefully memorable trip offshore to catch big Amberjack.

They will never forget it and neither will I.

Everything worked just right that trip.

Even better than you could hope for cause we spotted a good mark on the bottom machine when we were just cruising, and drifted three times over the hole and the boys cause major-sized grouper on the bandits.

Big fish, ten to twenty five pounders, both red and black grouper.

But we went on to the Amberjack hole and wore the fish out. The fish wore us and the boys out.

They caught forty pounders, sixty pounders, Little Mark caught an eighty-six pound A.J. on a rod-and-reel. The biggest ever caught on conventional gear on the ACE.

To make a long story short we had three hundred seventy-three pounds of grouper and eleven hundred forty pounds of Amberjack, and the young boys caught 'em all.

Us men just baited up the lines, coached, and gaffed the fish.

We're plodding home from the sixty miles offshore on the ACE.

A steady ten knots is all the ACE would do, loaded or unloaded.

It's a beautiful evening, calm, the sun going down, everybody's content and happy.

Back behind us we can see we are being overtaken at a high rate of speed by some sport fishermen in a Mako, or a Proline with a big outboard. Two guys heading in the same direction we are except at three or four times our speed.

The sports boat is coming around us on the west side, illuminated by the setting sun, two fishermen headed home and happy.

They slow down to our speed when they come along side, one guy is digging in the fish box, it's obvious they are going to show us something.

The fellow digging in the ice chest finally finds what he's looking for and lifts it up over his head with both hands. The guy driving the boat is giving us the thumbs-up sign, excited and proud.

What they're holding up is a good-sized Red-Grouper, probably twenty pounds, and they are obviously bragging on the capture of such a fine fish.

We're giving the thumbs-up sign too, acknowledging their good fortune but I'm motioning for them to wait before they take off at full speed and I'm giving instructions to our young crew-boys to dig out one of their fish from our ice boxes on the ACE.

The idea catches on quick and the sports boat is idling alongside at twenty yards and our boys are scrambling.

I'm having to help get the fish out of the box, one of many big A.J.s, and these boys finally get their fish out to hold up and show-off, and it takes three of 'em to do it, cause what they're holding up is a ninety-five pound Amberjack that's five feet long and it's all four young boys can do to lift it up to show over the rails.

You can see the two grown men in the sports boat kinda deflate a little bit, their bodies visibly sag cause we can see 'em real good silhouetted by the setting sun.

They unceremoniously dump their prize catch back in their ice box and pour the coal to their outboard, leaving us behind like the hare left the tortoise.

I know those boys in the sportsfishing boat wished they had just blown on by us. By slowing down to show-out they had let us steal their thunder, pop their bubble, blow their ego and claim the bragging rights.

I bet when they were showing their nice fish off at the dock, and to family and friends, they never mentioned that old slow white boat, full of children and big fish.

Coons

One of my good friends once said that if a coon weighed one hundred pounds, there wouldn't be anyone living in Florida. I think he's right cause they would steal all your food or they'd break in your house and eat you while you were in bed.

They are cute, smart and one of the most destructive animals on earth, wild or as a pet.

Here's some of the coons I've known.

We had a little baby coon once that we named "Rabies" and when someone new would pick 'em up, cuddle and pet 'em, and then ask his name, we'd say, "Rabies" and they'd throw that coon down like a hot rock.

Rabies climbed up a tree and escaped as a child, before he could do much damage.

Another new coon encounter was when I came to work one morning and there was blood and fur scattered all around the fish house floor. Then I found a dead coon floating in the canal and wondered what had gone on.

I knew that my fishing partner J.R., had been down here cleaning eight hundred pounds of mullet the night before, so I called 'em.

Here's what he told me happened.

At about 2 a.m. he was down to his last fifty pounds of fish to filet, dumped out on the cleaning table where he'd been cutting 'em and dropping the fish heads in a basket at his feet.

J.R. said he was tired out from fishing all day and cleaning fish all night, in sort of a stupor from exhaustion and the quietness of Spring Creek at that hour. Said he had to reach way across the cleaning table to reach a mullet that had almost slid off. As he did that he stuck his leg a little further under the cleaning table and something grabbed his pants leg, started shaking it and growling.

J.R. wakes up real quick, yelling out and jumping back, dragging a fat boar coon from under the table attached to his pants.

The coon turns loose, arches his back, bows-up and growls at J.R.

J.R. grabs a three-foot steel drag hook hanging from the rafters over his head and whacks the coon hard, trying to kill 'em for scaring him so, thinking he'll run off.

But the blow the coon took seemed to make 'em mad and he decided to fight, growling louder and not retreating.

I guess that coon really wanted those mullet heads in that basket, cause he and J.R. fought all over that fish house by the signs of it, J.R. telling me that coon wouldn't quit even with 'em beating 'em with the drag hook, him growling and hissing and trying to bite 'em.

They finally fought over to the dock where J.R. knocked the coon down and kicked 'em in the water.

J.R. said the coon didn't give up then, still growling and cussing, trying to swim, and J.R. said he himself had been caught-up in the battle and that he finally laid down on the dock and beat that mean attack-coon floating in the water till he quit his cussing, swimming and breathing.

Coons chewed a hole through one-inch thick pine cabin doors on the ACE to lick the grease from the frying pan that we cook our smoked link sausage in. That particular batch of venison sausage the coons chewed the door up after, was probably the best sausage I ever ate, worth gnawing your way through wood for.

Dog Island coons really became a problem when one of the wily devils figured out how to poke holes in screens, heavy gauge aluminum screen-wire at that.

Since we didn't have air conditioning in the cottage we kept the doors open out onto the big screen porches day and night. Some mornings we'd get up and all our Oreos or Chips-Ahoy would have been devoured on the kitchen counter. Empty torn bread sacks scattered on the porches and in the yard, since some of the coons preferred to get theirs to-go, rather than eat in.

More than once we had guests awake to uninvited and unwanted furry guests quietly nibbling up the remains of a candy bar or other unfinished night-time snacks, left on the bedside table two feet from your head.

This even seemed to upset and scare some people and they didn't want to visit anymore.

I just didn't eat in bed much and they never bothered me while I was trying to sleep.

Except one nite when we had made it to the island late and there was a coon-hole on the porch that I was too tired to fix.

We ate dinner and went to bed where I instantly fell into a deep sleep, only to be awakened by hollering and yelling and the pounding of feet running on wood.

Jumping up outta bed in my drawers, I stagger into the main room half asleep to find my son, Ben, tugging on the back end of a loaf of Merita and ole he-coon pulling on the twisty-tie end. The loaf of bread has already been pulled half-way through the screen by the coon on the outside of the house on the steps, and he doesn't want to give up his prize but finally retreats at the arrival of reinforcements lead by me, yelling now and mad at being woken up, grabbing my rifle out of the closet, but the coon's long gone by the time I get there and Ben's holding our mangled Merita up and it looks like a ripped-up chicken that dogs had fought over.

I'm wide awake now and bent on solving this screen-tearing problem, patching up the entry hole they'd been using, checking around the house for coons, wanting to shoot one for all the trouble they'd caused.

The house finally quiets back down and everyone goes to sleep except me, and I'm laying on the couch with the lights out, propped up where I can see the back porch in the moon light. My trusty .22 rifle laying on the floor beside me.

I drift off and start cat-napping when a light scratching noise makes me open my eyes.

And there he is.

The breaking and entering expert.

The screen ripper.

The bread and cookie stealing ring-tailed ringleader.

And he's brought back-up with 'em cause there's three more coons sitting on the steps waiting on the master to perform his magic by opening the screen to let them in.

And the lead coon had learned a trick and I watched 'em use it.

First the ole coon would take his paw and hook a couple of claws in the screen wire and twist back and forth till he broke a couple of wires, then he'd push and twist with his paw till he'd worked his front leg through the hole. When he had a nickel to a quarter sized hole poked in the screen he'd take his leg out and push his nose in the hole to make it bigger till he could get his head through.

When I had seen how he'd been tearing in, I showed the old coon that I could poke holes in screens too, cause I shot that coon right through the screen he'd been tearing up.

Ever since shooting that one coon we never had one tear holes in the screens again.

I guess old screen-tearer never taught anybody his trade, and I'm glad he didn't.

We played coon-lotto every night that we went to the dump with our garbage. Everybody making a guess as to how many coons would jump outta the dumpster. Usually the guesses would range from seven to twenty-five or so and sometimes there were too many jumping-out-too-fast to count 'em all.

The coons plagued our garbage at the restaurant, us trapping 'em, shooting 'em, killing any and all we could and they still stayed ahead of us.

We had a raccoon rodeo once with us running a half-grown coon up a short support pole in front of the motel. Mabry, Ben's dog, was barking at it and the coon was hissing back when Ben knocked the coon off the pole with a shovel into the azalea bed, Mabry diving in after the coon.

Barking and howling, hissing and growling is coming out of that thick flower bed, bushes are shaking and there's lots of commotion when all of a sudden ole Mabry breaks out into the parking lot and she looks just like a bucking bronco at a rodeo, raising up on her back legs and pawing at her ears, hopping stiff legged, standing on her front legs and kicking her back legs high.

Little Coon looks just like a champion cowboy bronc rider with his back legs spradding Mabry's neck, holding on to Mabry's ears with his front paws and his teeth buried in the fur on top of Mabry's head.

Lord what a sight they were dancing, twirling, running, swirling, Mabry growling and squealing and the coon hanging on for the grand prize.

Mabry finally bolted off into the dark with the coon still in the saddle.

She came back about ten minutes later with no visible damage.

We don't know what happened to the coon but I figure he got away. I think Mabry was just glad to get rid of 'em.

Here's a childhood coon experience that's sorta pagan-like, but I guess that's how some of us young boys were for a while.

I was in the Boy Scouts for a short time and we went to the Okeefenokee Swamp on a camping trip. Pitched our pup-tents on Billy's Island where I guess most all the troops camped over the years, cause the coons were well-trained persistent thieves and there was an infestation of 'em. We even saw a few of 'em scurrying around in the daytime, I guess they were anxious for the night time feeding and festivities.

The Scout Master warned us to guard our food and keep it in our little tents close at hand.

Dark came and we roasted our wieners and marshmallows and slid into our sleeping bags inside our pup-tents, planning on going to sleep.

And a pup-tent is a good name for those little canvas shelters we were to sleep in cause there was just enough room for two sleeping bags to lay side-by-side and a little triangle shaped area at the end of the tent to store our gear and groceries which was right by our heads.

As soon as the camp quieted down and me and my tent-mate were zipped-up in our bags, I started hearing little rustling sounds in the area behind my head where our precious groceries were stored. (Bread, cookies, canned meat, more cookies, candy bars and more cookies). Quite an unnerving sound in a pitch dark tent in the middle of a swamp.

Me and my tent-mate didn't say anything yet, neither wanting to make out like we were scared or anything.

But when the sound of paper being torn and the sound of munching and crunching by teeth on crisp cookies starts, something's got to go and that was us screaming and yelling bolting out the front flap of the tent, only shining our flashlites at the perpetrator after we're standing outside, clad only in our underwear and socks, and lighting up two or three sets of coon eyes gorging on our groceries in the back of our tent.

And we're not the only ones.

Boys all around the campsite are boiling out of their tents yelling, some crying for momma, all invaded by the coons.

Fright turns to mad and mad turns to rage as I grabbed an oak limb and attacked the varmints that so scared me and are eating my food.

Flashlights are shining all over the area and coons by the dozens are bolting everywhere, being chased by crazed and scared young boys with sticks and tent-poles and the battle is engaged.

All the coons escape to the woods with the exception of one big fat coon that must have liked the cookies too much and ate too long cause he's the last one to bolt from a tent and all of the two dozen enraged Boy Scouts take hot pursuit after that gluttonous coon, kicking at 'em; striking 'em with sticks, keeping flashlite beams on 'em and everybody gathering in an uncontrolled mob, screaming and yelling chasing that one unfortunate coon through the campsite.

The Scout Masters are hollering at us to stop but the madness is upon us and we can't stop, we're in the hunt, the bloodlust is upon us and that coon is going to pay for the sins of the whole raccoon clan.

The coon fought hard but he was outnumbered and surrounded. We kicked and beat and he hissed and growled and bit and scratched.

The ole coon finally fought his way into the waters of the swamp and we went right into the water with 'em, beating and flailing with our sticks, finally whopping that coon in the water so many times with oak limbs and pine sticks that he was dead.

And when the Scout Masters finally caught up with us and lifted the coon by the tail out of the water, we cheered. The demon was done and victory was ours.

And to make the lesson complete we were instructed to build up the main campfire while the Scout-Masters skinned the coon, and we ran a green oak limb through that now dressed coon and roasted that cookie-fed devil over the open flames and everybody got to eat a piece of burnt-raw coon meat.

And I'd say that meat tasted real good to this day, though I haven't eaten one since.

Coons are nothing but trouble.

SHRIMPING   CLAY MARSHALL LOVEL

40

Shrimping

We never got into it big-time.

Never got into the big-boat shrimping, the forty to seventy foot rigs, pulling two or four, fifty-foot nets.

All of us around Spring Creek used our multi-purpose mullet skiffs and everybody rigged their boats out different to pull little twenty-five and thirty foot shrimp nets. Only capable of pulling one net with an outboard motor.

I had two small steel outriggers that I bolted to the rear bulk head of our mullet boat, and I would pull each "door" on the shrimp net from an outrigger and it helped me spread my net which was a flat, three seam net that looked like a twenty-five foot wide butterfly net, straining water through the webbing and retaining the shrimp and other sea creatures that are spooked off of the bottom by the "tickle chain", a piece of heavy chain that's attached to each door of the net and hangs lower than the leadline and lightly brushes the bottom making the shrimp scoot up into the water column so the net can scoop 'em up.

We're fishing for hoppers, the night-time shrimp, that show up in our bays in late March and hang around till May. They raise up in the canals and grass flats, looking like tiny translucent grasshoppers, hanging upside down on the old pilings and seawalls like bats, till they get big enough to move into the bay where they stay buried in the muddy bottom during the day and move around at nite to where we can catch 'em.

They grow fast in the bay, doubling their size twice every moon, getting big enough to eat.

Big enough to be eaten by everything.

Everything that walks, swims or flies like to eat shrimp.

And we liked to catch 'em, for food and money.

And it was work. Work that usually came after a full day-light day of work.

Here's how it went.

Get in the bay and get set-up right at sundown, maybe throw out a buoy or two to mark areas we want to drag and keep us from hitting oyster bars when it is black dark.

To drag before full dark was pretty much a waste unless the water was real muddy from a hard blow.

You tie the tail bag up tight with a special knot that can be jerked undone when the bag's full to dump it. The tail bag is dropped over the stern with the boat moving ahead, then the net is slowly drug off the net table till it's pulling tight on the doors and then they're lowered into the water and rope is played out till the net is spread wide and fishing.

One hour drags is what we made, taking turns each drag, one time being the boat driver, the next being the take-up and cull man.

The cull man was the best end of the deal. Taking the net up, pulling the swelled-out tail bag up on the net table, untying it and dumping the contents out, hearing the sound and feeling the feel of dozens and dozens of shrimp hopping and popping and bouncing around your legs, squirting around like a bunch of sideways fleas. You know you had a good tow when the shrimp are spilling out of the dump-box and all you want to do is get the bag tied-up again and back overboard so you can catch more.

Get the net deployed again and drag the same territory quick cause we know how it goes, how quick the shrimp can disappear or move.

A typical one hour tow on good bottom can give a man all he can do to cull everything out of the pile of seaweed, trash fish, stingrays and no-telling-what.

Cull out ten or fifteen pounds of pretty hoppers, beautiful gold and honey colored shrimp with one dot on each side of their tail. We are happy with that many for an hour's work. We're also happy with some of the valuable by-catch that we save besides the shrimp. Two little flounders about hand sized and one big soft-shell crab about six inches wide across his back.

When we're settled into our next drag with the net out we turn the deck lite on. I take the tiller and let Bruce work his magic with the Coleman stove we've got on board. He fires it up and puts some peanut oil into a 10 inch black iron spider, or frying pan, letting the grease get hot while he scales those little flounders and peels the back off that soft shell, rinsing those fresh fish and crab in the salt water that's flowing by the boat.

Some salt and pepper, a little corn meal dusted over those three critters and into the hot grease they go.

Two o'clock in the morning, a cool, jacket-wearing, crystal clear early spring night, dragging a shrimp net about three miles an hour with a light breeze blowing at the same speed and direction of the boat, keeping the smells and the steam and the heat from those frying fish in the boat with you, making your mouth water with anticipation.

Lord it smells good.

Good God Almighty it tastes and feels good. That warm delicious fish and crab settling in your cold empty belly and now another smell getting your interest as Bruce has replaced the frying pan with a pot of seawater boiling on the stove and a couple dozen live hoppers dumping in to cook.

That little fried flounder, handed to you too hot to eat but you eat 'em anyway pulling his fins off and nibbling the meat off the sides of 'em, his naked back bone still steaming when you toss it overboard.

We share a cup of hot coffee when we share that soft shell crab, and when the crab's gone we're licking the grease and cornmeal off our fingers eyeing those boiling shrimp.

We cool the boiled shrimp down with some fresh seawater and eat those in a hurry cause it's time to take up the net again.

Pull the tow rope in, hoist the doors out of the water, drag the net down to rinse the mud out of the bag and all the shrimp hung in the wings of the net down to the tail bag.

Dump out the catch.

Deploy the net.

Cull through the catch, saving all the valuables and pitching the by-catch overboard.

Hour after hour after hour.

Repeating the above until the sun comes up or you just can't stay awake anymore.

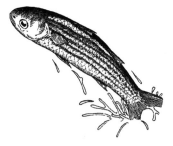

Doggie-Do Christmas Tree

Momma told me I could go hunt us up a Christmas tree.

I was finally old enough to take an axe and go pick out a nice tree for us to decorate. I was peacock-proud and going to find the best one ever.

In North Florida it's not unusual to use a nice loblolly or slash pine for a Christmas tree and there were plenty of 'em.

I must of scrutinized and sized-up two or three hundred different pines before I found one that had just the right shape and form. I had also worked my way a good mile or so from the house before that lucky-sacred evergreen presented itself to me.

It was perfect, a little too big maybe, but we would trim it down when Daddy got home and boy would he be proud at the tree I'd found. Momma and my brother and sister would love it too.

Chop and whack, whack and chop with that old axe.

Finally the tree falls over and I have to whack a few more times to get it completely free from the stump.

Time to drag it home like you see pictures of on paintings and on Christmas cards, an axe in one hand and a nice tree following along behind.

Well a green pine tree's heavy, even though only ten-feet tall, specially when it's full like a picture-perfect Christmas tree should be.

It's especially heavy and really wide when you're trying to drag it through some thick, briar-infested woods back to the house.

Some places were so thick I'd have to lay the axe down so I could pull on the tree with both hands to get it to come along through the thick brush.

45

Sometimes I'd have to take the axe and cut down some saplings so I could get it through at all.

I sweated and panted and cussed and rested and pulled, tugged, drug, twisted and wrestled that tree all the way to the house. Exhausted, bug-bit, briar-scratched, with blistered hands from all the cutting and pulling. Sap stained, whipped but triumphant I burst in the house and told everybody to come look at the pretty Christmas tree I'd brought home.

Everybody ooohed and aaahed over that pretty pine laying on the ground and then somebody stood it up to see how it looked from all sides and then the odor appeared.

That all too familiar, unmistakable smell of fresh dog-crap like when you've got it up to your ankles on your shoes and don't know it, until you get in your car and shut the door.

My beautiful tree, my first solo Christmas pine was fouled from the lower branches to the tip-top, pine-nettles glued together on the side that was down, from being drug through a pile of fresh doggie-do that must have been laid by a five hundred pound dog.

My tree spent Christmas on the burn pile and me and Daddy went and got another one the next day.

I never have liked dogs much since then.

46

Ben and Little Mark

(Part of the Learning Phase)

I was cleaning mullet down at the fish house one late summer afternoon.

Nice breeze off the creek blowing up the canal, keeping me cool and the bugs away.

Grab a scaled mullet, cut his head off, flip 'em over and cut the filet from the head-end to the tail in one slash. Spread the fish out flat and pull the guts out. Slice thru the belly and throw the filet in the slush water. Lay the fish backbone down on the cutting board, slice off the remaining filet from tail-end to head and throw both the backbone and the filet in the pan and grab another mullet.

That's what I was doing, and in-between each mullet I'd glance up the canal.

And glance again.

And look hard that way again.

Knowing Ben and Little Mark ought to be coming in anytime, should have been in long ago.

I had just started letting Ben and Clay take the tunnel-boat, our gill-net boat, the mullet skiff involved in a lot of our previous stories, out net-fishing by themselves.

I was hoping they'd come in soon or I was going out looking for 'em.

Then I see my ole mullet skiff sorta slide into the canal.

But there wasn't much boat sticking up outta the water, just the bow.

And Little Mark was holding on to the light-pole with one hand, leaning hard to one side like the sailboaters that race on T.V. do, when they are trying to keep the boat from tipping over.

And that's what Little Mark was trying to do, keep

47

the boat from rolling over cause it was full of fish and water.

I mean full.

Full to where if they hadn't kept the boat moving forward and if they had slowed down in deep water, the wake behind 'em would have raised the stern up and shoved the bow under, and the boat, boys, fish and all would have gone to the bottom.

But they made it to the boat ramp at the end of the canal and got the bow up on land so the motor wouldn't go under and the boys jumped outta the boat.

Happy, happy, happy to be back on land. They were yahooing and laughing and cutting up something fierce, so full of the event they had just experienced. They were so wound up that we had to calm 'em down to get the story out of 'em.

They had gone out to catch a load of jacks, Crevale Jack. Preferably the one to two pound size that bring good money as a food-fish in New York. The big Crevale Jacks from three pounds to fifty pounds are just crab bait and they tear our nets to pieces with their power and speed.

Anyway the boys went after some Jacks by themselves for the first time and what they had was a solid swinging load of L.Y.'s, or Menhaden, which are small, quarter-pound size fish that are hard to get out of the net and are worth only ten cents a pound as crab-bait.

The young boys were happy and excited for a few minutes cause they thought the battle was won and over when they had survived the boat sinking and being shark-eaten cause when you strike a good bunch of L.Y.'s you can't help but draw all the sharks in the neighborhood.

You see, L.Y.'s are an oily fish and when thousands of 'em go down on the net they fill almost every mesh in it and when you start taking up the net and piling it on the boat the fish start to pack and squish together and their oil and scent gets thick in the water and big sharks and little sharks show up like magic from everywhere and they're eating fish outta the net and their fins are slicing the water all around the net and when all the net is on the boat and the boat's level with the surface of the water and about to tip over cause it's loaded out of balance and the sharks are now circling the boat which is the source of all that good fish-oil smell, it can get exciting.

Instinct says it's time to level the boat quick and get gone from here.

And that's what they did.

Ben cranked the motor and got the boat moving so the L.Y. juice-filled water would flow out the back and Little Mark grabbed the pole and leveled her out. The sharks followed along easily as the boat couldn't make much time with the load it was carrying.

Anyway with some skill and some luck they made it back to the dock and thought the worst was over.

Welcome to the real world of commercial fishing. What they had just experienced was the fun part, the catching part. The cleaning and the packing are the work part of bait-fishing.

It's late afternoon in August, ninety-eight to a hundred degree temperature.

Not a breath of air moving.

The bright sunshine beaming straight up the canal to the boat ramp, heating the water, the black mud of the banks and the concrete of the ramp to about a hundred and ten degrees.

No shade what-so-ever, only a mullet-skiff loaded to the rails with eleven hundred and forty-eight pounds (remember, four to a pound, that's about four thousand five hundred and ninety-two fish), of L.Y.'s.

To be shaken and picked out of the net.

Shoveled-up, picked-up and scooped up and put into bright-orange fish baskets.

Loaded into the back of a pick-up truck and backed

up to the fish house and unloaded.

Twenty-four cardboard and wax fish-boxes have to be folded and assembled.

Twenty-four cardboard and wax lids for those fish boxes have to be made-up.

Twenty-four clear plastic liners have to be installed in each fish box.

The L.Y.'s have to be weighed-up into fifty-pound lots, then rinsed and chilled in a slush of water and ice, then poured into the plastic lined box. The plastic folded over the fish, the lid put on and then you pick the fifty-pound box up and tote it to the freezer.

Hot, slippery, nasty, stinky, strenuous back-breaking work till the twenty-third and last box is neatly stacked in the freezer.

Then to wash all the fish-baskets out and hose down the fish-house floor.

Then to bail out the L.Y. juice filled mullet-skiff with a bail-cup made from a Clorox jug, rinse the boat with the water hose and bail it out again.

Now the adventure is about over when the boat's tied-up in its slip. Pure exhaustion is the main emotion showing thru the sunburn and mud. Fish scales are in their hair and they both smell like crab-bait.

But it's settle-up time, pay day, time for the money to be split for the big catch and all the labor.

Spirits rise, smiles crack out on the boy-men faces.

Here comes the big money, cash.

The grand total is One Hundred and Fourteen dollars and eighty cents.

$114.80

And we have to deduct the gas, oil and drinks as expenses which we agree on to be about ten dollars.

Leaving $104.80.

And I get one-third of the catch as the boat owner, which amounts to $34.90.

And they each got $34.90.

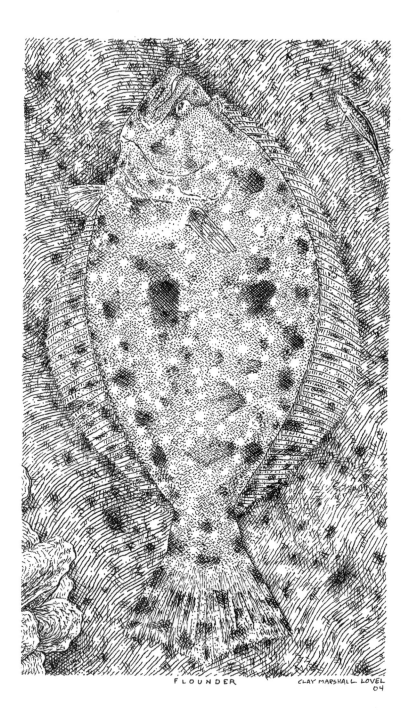

FLOUNDER

CLAY MARSHALL LOVEL
04

Flounder

A fish like no other.

A fish that's flat as your shoe sole, a filet-of-sole I think it's called at high-end restaurants up north.

Flounder is a good name for a fish that lays as flat as a plate on a table, brown-splotched camo color on his top side and snow white on his bottom side, fins running the length of his body, an expandable mouth full of long sharp teeth and the strangest thing of all, both eyes stare up from the same side of its head. Not born that way, with both eyes on the same side like a regular fish, as a juvenile they're on either side, as they mature the eyes grow over that way.

A night creature.

A creature you rarely see in the daytime. A water animal that flutters and creeps up to the shoreline and onto the oyster bars after the sun goes down. A fish that rises with the tide, moving up into a couple of inches of water to stare straight up with both eyes, even though it's laying on its belly, waiting for any fish, shrimp or crab to come by and make its dinner.

Waiting for us to come by with a bright spotlight and a heavy four-pronged gig and stick 'em and hoist 'em in the boat.

A magical experience for those that haven't done it much, a still special experience for those of us that have done it a lot.

Night time on the water.

There's nothing like it, especially on a perfect flounder night. A night with no moon, no wind, a low tide with it starting to rise. The oyster bars are sticking up three feet or more and the water is clear.

You are usually poling the boat along a good shoreline with a shelly bottom, looking in two to ten inches of water for a mashed-flat football outline of a flounder, looking at a lot of other sea creatures too, that act so differently at night, and you need a dark moonless night, the fish hold better to the spotlight when there's no moon.

Everywhere you look there's a pinfish or butterfish or a stingray, motionless, oblivious to the light you're shining on them, frozen in their liquid space for you to study.

Mullet glide in and out of the circle of light, sometimes jumping at the light and landing in the boat.

Redfish laying in 6 inches of water, just begging you to gig 'em only you know better unless you've got some back-up gig to flounder with, cause those big reds will tear the gig-head off your pole leaving you just a stick with no points.

Sheephead, sometimes two or three of 'em, banked up around rock or an old crab trap and big sheephead are worse than the redfish about tearing up your gear.

Then there he is.

A flounder.

A nice dinner sized one about two pounds or so, laying in about four inches of water. Just his eyes showing with a light dusting of sand covering his body, only his outline showing, laying in ambush for about anything that swims close.

Except we're about to ambush him.

Don't draw back to stick 'em like, an Indian throwing his spear.

Ease the prongs of your gig right down to 'em, keeping the light steady on 'em all the time.

Don't dare lightly touch 'em with the gig before you stick 'em cause he'll be gone in a flash, but when you're an inch or two away thrust it hard all the way thru 'em into the bottom and hold on.

The mud will boil and the gig handle will shake and if you use a clean sweeping motion you just swing 'em in the boat, stand on 'em with your feet and pull the gig out.

Then you throw 'em in the ice box and start looking for another one. Usually where there's one there's more.

The hunt is on.

Here's a story about the most we ever gigged.

It was on my birthday, which is early July, I don't remember which birthday but between twenty-five and forty.

We're on Dog Island, it's eight p.m. the tide's falling hard. It's been a pretty pretty day, hot and clear. We've caught, cleaned and fried some mullet with some taters and slaw.

It's not beginning to get dark yet and we've come to go floundering. We're full, sleepy and tired, so we set the clock for twelve-thirty a.m. when the tide's started back in.

Believe it or not we get up when the alarm goes off and head down to the ferry dock where we keep the little twelve foot aluminum boat we flounder out of.

We paddle across the cove to the shoreline, get out, hook-up our spot lights, get our gigs out and start dragging the boat behind us shining in the shallow water.

"There's one," I say as soon as I clip my light wires to the battery.

Bobby gets a gig out of the boat and sticks 'em.

"Here's another one," Mark says as he sticks his gig in 'em, "and there's two more right beside 'em."

And that's how the night went, or should I say the morning cause it was one-thirty or two o'clock when we got started, we couldn't go thirty feet without finding one or two. Some of the flounder were so close to the dry shoreline that just from the light motion of ocean, their backs would almost be exposed.

When we made it to the old ballast pile with scattered rock and sand there were more flounder than we could look at with two spotlights, we'd step on one going to gig another one.

We shined and gigged and gigged and shined till the

box was full and there were flounder all over the bottom of the boat and we would have gigged more but we couldn't get 'em to hold to the light anymore cause the sun was coming up and we hadn't even noticed.

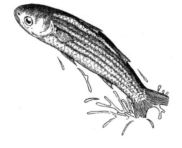

Floundering Part Two

We took all the young boys floundering a *few* times.

I guarantee that all our sons and nephews that were ever there on Dog Island have never forgotten those nighttime trips, the things they saw, the adventures they had.

The youngsters always wanted to gig flounder, and during the day, us Daddy's always thought we wanted to go too.

Till we got a little older and tireder.

About nine o'clock the young boys would be all fired-up to go gig fish, shine the light in the water, chase alligators, spear sheephead, reds, crabs, mullet, anything that would sit still long enough. They would be asking "When are we leaving? Is it time yet? You want us to load the truck?"

Mark and I, had had it.

We had worked all day long, moved everybody and everything by boat to the island, caught and cleaned fish, cooked 'em, had a few drinks, eaten fish with all the trimmings, showered and were sitting in rocking chairs on the porch, watching the orange blues, purples and pinks of the after-sunset, before full dark.

The breeze blowing thru the screens cooling us.

I'm not going anywhere but to bed.

So we had to make excuses about not taking 'em floundering.

"Boys the tide ain't right."

"The moon's wrong."

"It's blowing too hard."

"The batteries aren't charged"

"We forgot the new bulbs."

"WE'LL GO TOMORROW NIGHT."

All the excuses were made to the wails and complaints of the boys that still had plenty of energy to go, wanted to go now and couldn't understand why we didn't go.

But we didn't.

We couldn't.

We were give out.

I sure was glad when the boys got old enough to go by themselves cause getting ready to go "Floundering" got to be a big joke and still is today to a few of us twenty years later.

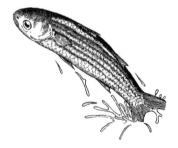

Frog Gigging

Always heard 'em bellowing at night down on the lake in the summertime.

We didn't have any air-conditioning back then. I'd have the windows wide open hoping for a breeze. The covers on the bed would be thrown back and I'd be laying there, covered with a light coal of sweat, trying to get cool enough to go to sleep, listening to the thoughts in my head and the summer-night sounds outside.

The cicadas would be screeching in a side to side cadence with the crickets, tree-frogs and grasshoppers in constant back-up.

Then you'd hear the non-cadence, spasmodic, no two sound the same, croak or moan or half-bark-bellow of the bullfrog.

And then you'd hear one answer, then you'd hear a third bullfrog and maybe a fourth join in and they'd all be croaking like crazy then they'd all shut up.

Listening to 'em would make me want to go get some cause they were real good to eat and a challenge to catch.

Nighttime is the only time to catch 'em.

The darker the better.

Bright moonlight nights make it where they don't want to hold to a light real good.

Gigs, lights and a good eye for snakes are the basic equipment.

You can wade after 'em but floating along in a boat seems the best way to gig a bunch of frogs.

We once found a holding pond on the backside of a new subdivision that was absolutely full of grown bullfrogs. The most I'd ever seen. Too many actually. So many that they would be lined up in a row, side by side all the way around the clean-banked pond, looking like giant green spear-points with legs and glowing eyes.

When you'd gig the first frog you came to, (shining a spotlight in his face to make 'em sit still), it would spook the bullfrog sitting right beside 'em, that would let out an alarm chirp and jump in the water, which in turn would also spook the rest of the frogs sitting around, and you could stand there and watch and listen til all the frog chirped and cheeped and jumped like live dominoes back into the pond to safety.

The frogs would eventually come up and float on the surface with just their eyes sticking out of the water.

We'd try to gig 'em from the bank of the pond but weren't too successful cause with the frogs just being suspended in the water and us trying to gig 'em from an angle it was hard to get the gig stuck in 'em good.

We tried a new frog-gigging tactic.

We got us a little aluminum boat that we could tote to the pond and then we would purposely scare all the frogs into the water.

We get into the boat and float around in the dark, being real quiet.

Every two or three minutes we'd turn on our spotlight and look into the water.

There would be three or four big bullfrogs right beside the boat with their eyes glowing and their big meaty big legs spread out behind 'em, suspended by the water.

Now we could drive our five-pronged gigs straight down on our prey, with a lot of force and come up with a fat writhing bullfrog every time.

Turn off the light.

Wait a minute or so.

Turn it back on and gig a frog or two each time. As many as you wanted to gig you could get in about thirty minutes. They'd be jumping out of the sack we kept 'em in, (usually one of Momma's pillowcases I'd snuck out of the house), we'd have so many frogs stuffed in it.

Word of advice.

Do not gig snakes.

Do not let your friends gig any snakes, and caution first-time froggers not to gig snakes cause snakes are impossible to get off the gig prongs.

To even get a frog off of a gig you have got to jerk and snatch with your hands or stand on 'em with your feet to get the barbs pulled loose.

When you stick gigs in snakes they tend to get mad, and start striking anything and everything including themselves, and they writhe around and twist themselves in a constantly moving-hissing-ball around the part of their body that's got the gig stuck in it.

About all you can do is throw the gig away til the snake rots off, cause he will bite you three thousand times a second if you try to get 'em off alive.

Remember, if you got a lot of frogs you got a lot of snakes and probably alligators too.

Do not try to gig alligators either.

You can't hardly hurt 'em with a frog gig. All you do is aggravate 'em, make 'em mean and nasty and they scare the frogs away with all the commotion they make from getting stuck.

They bend the prongs real bad on your gig, sometimes tearing the gig-head off the pole, ending your night's frogging.

We used to just skin and eat the big back legs of the bullfrogs we caught.

One night we didn't think we had gigged enough frog for the amount of people we intended to feed so we got to looking harder at the few frogs we had caught. The more we looked we realized that frogs, like a squirrel or a deer, had a backstrap, a tenderloin and a buncha good looking meat on his short stubby front legs. So we just cut his head off and skinned the whole animal.

We split 'em down the backbone longways and fried 'em up. Every bit of that critter on the front-end ate just

61

as good as those fat legs on the back. Some of it ate even better cause it got fried crispier.

From then on we cleaned and cooked the whole frog whether we had too many or not.

Another interesting story on fresh-frog eating.

My buddy Vince and I met up about dark one nite at Vince's daddy's Cuban restaurant. We were going out to gig some frogs later that evening.

Vince's daddy finds out what we're up to and tells us to go get a good mess of frogs, bring 'em back in before the restaurant closes and he'll have the cooks fry 'em up for us and we'll have a feast about closing time.

Vince and I go and gig a quick mess of frogs, come back and clean 'em in the parking lot. We take the fresh frog legs, (not even an hour old), thru the back door and give 'em to the cooks.

Me, Vince, Vince's pop and some other regular customers are sitting in the bar anticipating those hot, fried frog legs coming out of the kitchen.

What came out of the kitchen was all the cooks, dishwasher and bushelp, screaming their heads off, running out the serving door, wild-eyed, terrified, not looking back, leaving.

We found out later what had caused all their panic and horrification.

The kitchen help had all gathered around the fryer to watch the frog legs being cooked, cause they had never cooked or eaten any and were looking forward to it; curious.

Fresh frog legs tend to do strange things after you salt and pepper 'em, roll 'em in flour and lay 'em in hot grease.

They tend to jump outta the frying pan.

All by theirselves, just those single cut-off bullfrog legs without even the rest of the frog attached will jump back out of that hot grease.

So when those novice frog-fryers floured-up that

dozen or so legs and dumped 'em all at once in the pan and all those legs started jerking violently and jumping outta the pan and falling on the floor and twitching and flopping that was all the hired help could stand.

They had to go somewhere else in a hurry.

And we couldn't get 'em to come back and finish cooking even after we caught up with 'em and told 'em that they just had to hold the legs down with a fork, for a minute or two, til the legs stopped wiggling and they would cook up fine.

We had to finish cooking that meal ourselves.

Mr. Vince had to hire some new help the next day cause some of those folks never came back.

HURRICANES   CLAY MARSHALL LOVEL
                                              04

Hurricanes

We've been through two or three hurricanes in the years we've been on the gulf and have dealt with dozens of near misses which sometimes caused alot of flood damage, but nothing like the devastion of a direct hit.

I've always thought of hurricanes being like a shotgun in the spread of the murderous blast of wind that blows everything down, but it's more like a rifle shot, where the severe damage occurs, when you picture the size of the target. If you're twenty or thirty miles east or west you're spared total destruction and just have to deal with the flooding tidal-surge.

We've got our hurricane preparation procedures down pat from our numerous immersions.

Pull all the boats out and haul 'em up to Hurbert's Pasture.

Secure the ACE, tying the bowline off to a cabbage palm across the canal.

Take all the peeler crabs out of the vats and put 'em in traps in the canal. (You know the electricity is fixing to go off indefinitely).

Pack away a few hundred pounds of ice in chests, the ocean is fixing to be in the ice house, melting everything.

Put everything that's on the ground or on low shelves in the restaurant, up high.

Gather up all checkbooks, payroll information, important documents, photos and take 'em with you.

Three or four hours of "getting it on," you're pretty well ready to go at the drop of a hat. So now's the time to wait, usually down at the fish house where you can watch the tide rise and the wind increase.

And we're going to leave and go thirty miles north when the roads start to flood. We've learned our lessons about staying.

Hurricanes seem to always hit at night and when

you're waiting on 'em in the dark and the water's rising fast you can have some thrilling experiences wading around in it.

The most painful is the floating ants, that get in a flat furry looking mass, drifting in the current, all of 'em driven out of the ground with the rising water, gathering in an inch-deep pile on the very top of their ant bed, to be floated off when it covers with water.

Wade through a yard square of floating fire ants and see what happens, all those ants wanting to climb to higher ground, which is you.

Snakes are hunting some place out of the water and they're moving around a lot. Swimming across in your flashlite beam, floating by on boards or logs. Every kind of snake, rattlers, moccasins, oak snakes, green snakes, water snakes. Somebody ran over a six-foot rattle snake during Hurricane Kate that had a half-grown rabbit in his mouth.

There's real excitement in being thigh-high in rising ocean, wading back to the television to check the radar and see a big pine limb break off and tear a power line down, sending sparks flying, the popping line falling in the water you're wading in.

Makes you move real fast.

To see the limbs on our huge live oak trees bend and shake like warm rubber from the force of the wind reveals the power of the wind and the strength of oak.

You watch the water rising up through the spaces in the boards on the dock, and cover the dock in the matter of a minute. The water's beginning to flow north beside our parking lot like a creek exploring new territory, moving so quick you have to walk fast to keep up with it.

The water's rising fast, high tide is three hours away and the storm is still a hundred miles away.

The wind is a steady sixty to seventy miles an hour, howling, rain in sheets going by.

We're standing on the concrete slab at the fish house

which is normally four or five feet above high tide. It's four or five inches above the water now and it's coming fast.

A small boat breaks loose from somewhere and sails past, bouncing off of poles and trees but never stopping, headed for the woods.

The water is up over the slab and we're sitting on a bench watching it rise up our boots, knowing that it's time to go, but we can't.

And there was no need to stay cause there's nothing you can do once the wind and water gets so high. If a boat breaks loose you can't do anything with it.

And that powerline's still down in the water.

But we got lucky that time, the water only rose another two feet and we sat it out on top of the picnic table like a bunch of coons in a tree.

And we don't stay anymore.

But when we do come back after a storm it is a real surprise package, no two are alike, and you can tell way before you get to Spring Creek how high the water got.

It is not a good sign to see one of your six-foot chest freezers in the ditch, a half-mile from the restaurant or a mullet skiff hung-up in the azalea bushes in somebody's front yard.

The restaurant looks o.k., but there's a distinct high water line marked on the front door by the silt that's left on everything when the water recedes.

Other than the freezers inside the kitchen floated and rolled over, dumping their contents, everything's fine, just a big clean up, which we've perfected. Take a waterhose, wash everything down, suck it up with a wet-dry vac, spray the electrical outlets with WD-40, wait for the electricity to come back on.

Cleaning up outside is a major task cause there's logs, pilings, boats, every kind of furniture, appliances or anything that will float laying around with tons and tons and tons of dead marsh grass.

But that can be handled too, with tractors and front end loaders.

We've been real lucky even though we were flooded three times in one year.

That was the year of the storm of the century that came in March. A "blind hurricane" some folks call it around here, because it had no eye.

But a hurricane is what it was with devastating effects, killing many people just east of us around Steinhatchee.

Ben calling at about three thirty in the morning, telling me the town's underwater.

I got up from the deepest sleep, fumbled my way into my clothes and started driving the thirty miles south to the Creek, needing coffee bad.

I pull into the BP station to get a cup, open the door of my truck to get out and then dive back in slamming the door, thinking someone is shooting at me.

But nobody's shooting.

It's just the flag on the flagpole, snapping and cracking so loud in the gusting wind that it sounds like rifle shots.

I'm awake now and concerned, seeing that flag standing out in a solid sheet, popping on the ends.

I take off for Spring Creek as hard as I can go, noticing the wind's buffeting my truck.

Everything stays o.k. til I get just south of Woodville and a pine tree is blown down so quick in front of my truck that I don't have time to stop and drive right through the top of it.

I'm having to go slow now, curving around blow-downs, driving on the shoulders, avoiding power lines. I make it to Wakulla Station and there's cars lined up, too many trees down to get by.

Somebody with a chain saw shows up and we cut our way thru, making it to U.S. 98 where the shoulders of the road are wide and the hiway is clear.

The wind and the rain let you drive about thirty miles an hour but I'm going to get there and when I finally make the restaurant Ben's standing in the parking lot, and it's underwater.

Fortunately for us the tide didn't get in the buildings and all we had to do was tend to the boats so they didn't get hung on the dock when the big tide went out, and did it ever go out. Just at daylite the wind went north with a vengeance, blowing roofs and shingles off, emptying the flooded bay.

Then it started to snow.

And we really started to wonder what was going on with the weather.

From a surprise March hurricane wind and tide, summertime conditions, to a freezing cold blasting Norther complete with snow and we're in Florida.

I never try to guess Mother Nature anymore.

I just get out of her way when she's mad.

Hurricanes are one of those events that should remind us all, of how significant and in-control we humans really are.

A natural, annual weather condition that we can't influence or control in the very least. A combination of wind, rain and tide that can move anything in its path, wiping out lifetimes of effort and work in minutes with no bias, favoritism, discrimination or malice.

You can't reason with it, steer it, communicate with it or destroy it.

All you can do is respect it, prepare for it as best you can and get out of its way.

Come back and deal with what it's left you.

Shows you we ain't much.

Paw-Paw's New Teeth

Paw Paw was what we called 'em.

He wasn't kin by blood but he was Daddy's best friend's Daddy, and he was part of our lives at that time.

We loved 'em and respected 'em and knew he would pull a joke or two or do something unexpected at most anytime.

That evening we were sitting around the table eating dinner, Momma, Daddy, my brother and sister and me, I was 10 or 12, the oldest child.

Paw Paw knocks and comes in the kitchen door all at the same time. Nobody ever locked their doors then and we expected known guests to just come right in.

Paw Paw had never had any teeth, hadn't since we'd know 'em; but he sure did tonight and that's why he was here at suppertime to show 'em off cause he knew we'd be here.

He was kinda clacking 'em together, "snap, snap," lips pulled back in an exaggerated smile so you could see those pearly-white sets of chompers that he had.

He was proud of 'em, smiling big.

Momma's standing up inviting Paw Paw to sit down and eat with us, hugging his neck.

Daddy says, "Paw Paw, I see you finally got you some teeth, they look real good," putting another bite of mashed potatoes in his mouth.

We're right in the middle of dinner, eating hard and fast, specially us three hungry kids in front of this home-cooked meal, not much slowing down from eating other than to say hello, but watching and listening to Paw Paw.

Daddy asks, "Paw Paw where'd you get those new teeth?" as he's slicing up some roast beef on his plate.

Paw Paw's standing at the head of the table, still smiling big and says as sincere as could be, "You wouldn't believe it," sorta snapping and clacking those new teeth together, stretching his lips even wider. "I went down to Cooley's Funeral Home to visit an old friend who had died and I walked in the back room to say hello to George, the undertaker, when I spied a whole cardboard box fulla sets of teeth." He goes on, "George told me he was going to throw 'em away cause the good folks that had worn 'em didn't need 'em anymore, so I decided I'd see if I could use some of 'em."

Well we had all stopped eating, kinda caught up in Paw Paw's story, looking at 'em, knowing he was going to say something wild, and he didn't disappoint us.

Paw Paw says, "I had to try on fifteen or twenty pairs 'fore I found some that would fit, but I think these look pretty good, don't you?"

He's really clicking and snapping those second-hand funeral home teeth, smiling even bigger, proud of himself.

We're all bug-eyed and staring, mouth open, speechless, grossed-out.

Dinner was over.

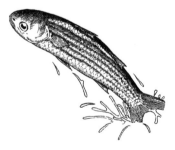

Curley Blue

Curley Blue was a teenager when I came to Spring Creek. I've been here twenty-five years and I think he's just coming out of that stage, but still a bit wild and unsettled.

Curley's family had North Carolina Renegade Indian blood in 'em strong, people of the swamp and sea, real outdoorsmen with some of the bunch kinda roguish.

The whole clan lived off the land for the most part. Catch as catch can. Fish some, work some, party a lot, fish some more when you're broke.

Curley got to be kind of legendary in a good and bad sort of way. He looked like an Indian except maybe a little tall, dark long hair, high cheekbones, thin and long legged, with a glint in his eye, looking way-off somewhere most the time. He couldn't read much or do math and this presented a problem at crew-share time trying to payoff and explain, but he could catch, kill, see, anticipate, shoot or run down anything that crawled, flew, ran, breathed or swam.

Here's a few stories I know about 'em.

Curley's clan ate deer meat all year long and they didn't freeze much meat, it was always fresh. I've cooked more than one fresh venison tenderloin on the ACE offshore, in July, that Curley would bring. Most all the deer they ate came off the right-of-way, at night, or out of the Refuge which was closed to hunting.

Curley's wife told me this story.

She and Curley were driving around, about noon, on some dirt roads that border the Refuge. It's June and hot and they're drinking beer, killing time, spending up the money from a good grouper catch the week before.

Two young does step out thirty yards in front of their car.

Curley stops and starts digging around in the glove

compartment, feeling around on the cluttered-up dash till he comes up with one, #1 buckshot to fit his trusty double-barrel twelve-gauge shotgun tucked under the seat.

He loads that gun, leans out the window, fires and lays one doe down in the road.

The other deer sorta hops back a few steps and then resumes staring at the yellow Chevy Nova, idling in the road and wonders why her companion is laying down.

Curley's wife said the deer is just sorta weaving and bobbing its head, with her ears up, looking at 'em when Curley separates the stock from the barrels on his shotgun, pitching the stock-part into the back seat and slides across her lap out the passenger side door like a snake slinking into the swamp, whispering, "sit tight, I'll be right back," taking the barrel part of that heavy twelve gauge with 'em.

Curley's wife is wondering what's going on and all the while the doe is just staring at the car, moving her head back and forth in curiosity. Then she sees Curley come out of the woods, behind the distracted doe and start slipping up to the deer.

Silent, long steps.

The doe's still looking at the car.

Curley's behind the doe with the twelve gauge barrels swung back behind his head like a baseball batter waiting on the pitch.

Curley's wife said she just couldn't hardly believe it even though she watched it. Curley laid one tremendous blow to the head of that ole doe with those barrels, killing it instantly. He grabs a deer by the ear with each hand, drags 'em both to the car, loads 'em in the trunk and off they go to buy more beer.

Once a guy in the pulpwood business told me another Curley Blue tale.

He told me that he and Curley were coming home from Taylor County when a turkey hen darted across the road in front of 'em, and he had to bring the car almost to a total stop to keep from hitting the bird.

Curley bails out the passenger side.

The turkey's running back and forth along an old broke down fence, panicked, hunting for a way across, forgetting she could fly for a minute, but finally hops, sorta flapping with her wings and takes off running in the woods.

Curley's only two steps behind the bird, leaping across the fence with a bound like a deer. And disappears like the turkey into the woods.

According to the pulpwooder the wait was short.

Curley and the turkey came back and the turkey was in his left hand still flapping and twitching. Curley was chuckling real low with a big smile on his face like "I told you so."

He was that good in the woods.

He was that good on the water, too.

Curley could spot a school of run mullet a half-hour before anybody else would see 'em coming. Everybody disbelieving till the fish would show up.

He could sit on the stern of the ACE, holding the end of a four hundred yard set of pompano net and tell us when a pompano would hit the net, able to tell the difference between a shark hit or a catfish, stingray or trout just by the vibration. He'd prove his case when we would take the net up and pick the fish out.

He could gig flounder even when the water was dark and steal baby gators out from under their momma's nose.

I once watched 'em run three coons down an oyster bar into the water at the far end. Then the coons decided to regroup and attack and chased Big-Bad Curley back to his skiff, shoving off fast.

Lightning scared Curley real bad.

I've seen 'em go hide under the bow of the ACE, cover his head with all the pillows and blankets and curl up like a child in bad thunderstorms offshore.

He's been in jail more than once.

Taking possession of anything not continually guarded has been a bad habit of his.

He'd get paroled, but it wouldn't be long before he would be in trouble again.

He drove one law enforcement officer crazy trying to catch 'em for violating his parole. This officer took it personal to apprehend Curley but he just couldn't do it. The lawman would get tipped off that Curley had snuck into his momma's house to eat dinner and they would get a posse up to encircle the place. The lawmen would get set up, yell out "Come out with your hands up, you're surrounded," and turn all their lights on.

Curley would come out alright, he'd throw open the back door, almost fly out with his first leap and bound like a frightened deer, taking six foot strides into the thick swamp and be gone before you could say "Stop."

The chase was over.

He was gone.

Melted, disappeared, evaporated, lost. No need to search or look cause Curley wasn't there anymore, he'd been absorbed into his element.

The law put the dogs on 'em once like hunters do a deer or a bear and the dogs got his scent, and they ran 'em from the Spring Creek Highway back east to the Shell Point Road. The officers stopped all traffic (including me) and I got to observe all the deputies on stands, man-stands instead of deer-stands, armed with shotguns, waiting for Curley to cross.

Curley got away.

He told me he sucked air through a reed, underwater in one of the sinkholes while the dogs got lost then he doubled back on his own scent trail.

He stayed loose for a year, living in the woods, sneaking off-shore fishing, eating at his momma's when he could. Stayed out of jail til he attended a big bonfire party at Shell Point beach where an undercover officer wearing a swimsuit pinned Curley down using a well-trained, mean looking, teeth filled German Shepard and got handcuffs on 'em.

Back to the pen he went. They fixed his bad teeth for 'em at state expense.

He got out after a year or so.

Got caught with a firearm, on the Refuge, out of season, on probation and back he went again.

Before he got sentenced the last time ole Curley had two five-foot diamond back rattlesnakes, in an aquarium, sitting on a table right beside his front door to greet all his guests with a frenzied singing duet of rattlers, following your every move with their heads, curled up ready to strike, sticking their tongues out at you.

Just Curley's way to say, "Welcome."

Curley could catch loads of mullet, was good deck hand help on a grouper or stone crab boat, a natural outdoorsman.

But the way Curley courted trouble made a natural "indoorsman" out of 'em.

RED BELLIES   CLAY MARSHALL LOVEL
                                                        04

Red Bellies

Red-eared Sunfish may be its professional classification but Red-Belly Bream is all I've ever known it as.

You won't find this critter in any lake or pond, he'll be in a fast-running creek or hard-flowing river. He will be in moving water.

The male Red-Belly is the only one with bright red or orange on 'em, the female fish is sort of a goldy color. The hue, brightness and color of both the male and the female seem to vary from creek to creek or river to river, their shape basically the same everywhere. They are more streamlined and more bullet shaped than a Bluegill or a Shellcracker, they're also a lot tastier than either of those fish, better fighters on a line.

Red-Bellies are a great fish, my favorite besides a mullet and the only type of fish I try to catch on hook-and-line.

On a cane pole, or a bream-buster, or an ultra-light spinning outfit and I only use crickets for bait. A wiggling, live, whole fresh cricket fattened on cabbage leaves, custom built for a #6 hook on light line.

To wade the Flint River with the water flowing around your legs and pitch a fat cricket into a slow-swirling eddy that's shaded by a 200-year old poplar or sycamore tree is almost a sure bet on hooking one. But if you miss the bite and your cricket gets his head or his butt bit-off don't bother throwing back in that hole to try to catch ole Red-Belly again, he don't like maimed or dead crickets.

You have to put another live one on the hook, then you can catch 'em.

Occasionally we throw flies at the Red-Bellies, sometimes poppin'-bugs, Beetle-Spins, earthworms, catawbas but mostly crickets. They are THE BAIT for a sure dinnertime catch.

When it's already 6 p.m. and we decide we want fresh bream for supper we just grab the cricket boxes, the rods and go down to the river and pick supper out of the water like picking squash from the garden.

Take those still twitching fish back up the hill to the house to scale 'em, cut their little heads off, salt and pepper 'em heavy, roll 'em in fresh ground cornmeal from a local mill and fry 'em a deep brown in peanut oil. Serve 'em with coleslaw and cheese grits, some fresh local peaches for dessert and it's as good as it gets.

You clean up the dishes and then everybody picks 'em a rocking chair on the porch. You look at stars for a while, watch the lightning-bugs come out, listen to the river roaring around the rock shoals. Your belly's full, your mind's at ease, it's time to go to bed and sleep like a baby.

That's Red-Belly Bream to me and mine.

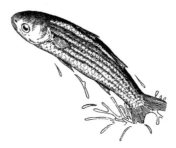

Antidote to Red Belly Bream

It was late summer, August probably, or maybe early September.

Clay and I went down to the river for a 6:30 p.m. meat-fishing trip, planning on frying up bream for supper about 8 p.m.

Ultra lite spinning rods, corks, hooks and crickets.

We figured we need a dozen to fifteen bream to cook cause there would be only four of us to feed.

We split up when we got in the river and fished hard in all the eddies and backwaters we could wade to.

The fishing was slow.

It was still hot for seven o'clock in the evening and the section of the river we were on flows from west to east letting the bright sunshine light-up all our favorite fishing holes, hurting supper-catching efforts.

Clay and I only had three or four fish between us and I could eat that many, so we started fishing our way up the river, wading up past the rapids to where the water slows, and the first dark shadows of evening shade the edge of the river bank.

Mary Jane and Bree climb down the ladder from the river bank to the shoals and wade up to where Clay and I are. The four of us have pretty much forgotten fishing for the moment, we're all just trying to soak up the beauty of the evening. The sound of the water rushing across the shoals, the shadows moving out from the green walled banks, the insects and frogs starting up their night sounds.

We got to quit all this nature-watching and get back to nature-catching.

I hook a cricket on, adjust my cork to about twelve inches deep and pitch it up to the shady bank handing the rod to Mary Jane.

The cork never stops. It floats to where it's over the sinker and keeps right on going underwater bending that ultra-light rod almost double, making that four-pound test line sing as it rips thru the water.

Mary Jane's laughing and reeling in a darting, splashing, hand-sized Red Belly.

Bree has commandeered Clay's fishing outfit and is casting to the same spot we had hooked the first fish. She lets out a whoop and a holler as she hooks-up too.

As fast as Clay and I can unhook a Red Belly and put new crickets on, the girls are hauling in hand-sized, half hand-sized, two-finger-size fish. We've got our supper quota in about five minutes and now we're just catching 'em and throwing 'em back.

The water's rushing around our legs, the rapids are roaring like the ocean, the orange sun-glow of late evening on the Flint muting colors and cares about anything but the moment, the fish, the happiness, the unbelievable bounty and beauty all inspired by Flint River Red Belly Bream.

TROPHY BASS   CLAY MARSHALL LOVEL
                                                04

Trophy Bass

Daddy caught the first Trophy Bass I ever saw.

He caught it with a Dalton Special on a Zebco 33, casting in the late afternoon off of Gridley's Dock.

Ten pounds twelve ounces it said in the local newspaper, The Tallahassee Democrat, accompanied by a three-by-five inch photograph of Daddy and the fish, taken at Red and Sam's Tackle Shop where you could buy shotgun shells for a nickel-a-piece back then.

That "Trophy Bass" of Daddy's held a coveted place in our freezer for years, taken out to display for neighbors and relatives that hadn't seen it yet, we couldn't afford the taxidermist.

I saw lots of Trophy Bass growing up and hunting and fishing around Lake Jackson. I saw 'em all the time actually. Most all of 'em I saw were hanging on a rope or a stringer being drug thru the grass on the right-of-way on U.S. 27, by old Black Men or Black Women. They'd have so many Trophy Bass that they couldn't tote 'em, some of 'em I'm sure were world records.

Those Black Folks knew how to catch lots of Trophy Bass, eighty to a hundred pounds of Bass a trip, having to walk and drag 'em, home with one hand and carry a fifteen-foot cane-pole as big around as your arm, with the other hand.

I caught some Trophy Bass, too.

I always liked mass-production in fishing and the trot-line was the thing to do.

You could bait that trot-line up, go off hunting or just messing around and come back in a few hours or the next day and your fish were caught for you.

We'd bait that trot-line with just about anything we could catch, but mostly small bream, so I guess that was why some days we'd drag trophy bass after trophy over the side of the boat.

We baited that trot-line with all sorts of things.

Little bream that we'd catch with cane poles using wasp larvae for bait. (Sometimes getting the nest away from the wasps was the trick)

We'd bait with gobs of earthworms dug outta the yard.

Crawfish from under the boat and in the ditches.

Frog, (toads don't work well) but tree frogs and bull frogs and big tad poles work great.

Lord we caught lots of Bass and Catfish, mudfish of giant proportions, water snakes, cotton-mouth moccasins, alligators and occasionally some kinda bird.

In the early Spring those Trophy Bass didn't like to bite. We couldn't catch many but we could sure see 'em.

They'd be on the bed, in the shallows among the weeds and the lily pads, in a place the ole Sow-Bass had fanned clean with her tail.

We'd have dozens of bass-beds spotted, and they'd drive us crazy not taking our fresh baits presented to 'em.

We'd pitch a live bream right in front of those Trophies and they just push 'em outta the bed.

We'd dangle globs of wiggling earthworms on her

nose, actually touching the fish with the bait and the old
Sow would turn around and blow the unwanted intruder
outta the bed with the fanning of her tail.

The live frogs we'd present would swim or hop away
from the fish on their own, not helping us out any.

Those bass wouldn't bite no matter what.

Couldn't get a gig into 'em, they wouldn't let you get
close enough.

But a .22 rifle would work if the water was shallow
enough.

That reminds me.

In the Oyster Bay community, that's just down the
shoreline from Spring Creek, lives a man in a house that
overlooks a deep hole in the edge of the bay. That hole
separates a long oyster bar from the Oyster Bay Man's
property, and he can see right down in that fishy hole
from his porch.

He told me there had been a Redfish, a big redfish
that he spotted laying up in the edge of the current.

Oyster Bay Man said he'd get excited seeing that big
fish hovering there and he'd go get his rod and reel and
climb down all those flights of stairs from his stilt-built
house, sneak into position, cast and see the redfish swim
off startled.

And he'd see the redfish back in the same place the
next day.

And Oyster Bay Man would make the attempt again
and have the same results.

And the same situation the next day with the same
results, and the next day and the next day, climbing up
and down those flights of stairs with the same
disappointing, frustrating results.

Oyster Bay Man told me he made one more attempt
on being the "sportsman". The fish swam off as usual and
the man said he cussed and stomped and said "to hell
with 'em I'm through," and then the Oyster Bay Man
brightens up and smiles at me and says, "he weighed

sixteen pounds he did" showing me with his hands spread how long he was.

"Congratulations," I said, "You finally caught 'em."

"No, no, no," Oyster Bay Man says laughing, "I shot 'em with a 30:06 rifle at low water the next morning and dipped 'em up with a net."

It's amazing what a person will do to capture a big fish if he can see it.

Back to Trophy Bass.

I can promise you that the trophiest of Trophy Bass was caught on a large cane pole, snatched outta the water like a tuna before he could jump or run or whistle. That fish was caught by country folks, not looking for sport but wanting something to eat.

Then that Trophy Bass was taken home, celebrated over as he was being scaled and cut into finger-size strips, fried in pure lard, and his head fed to the hogs.

"Trophy Bass" may be the modern translation of the southern term "More Food".

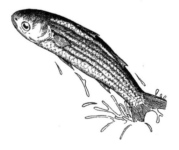

Florida Cracker

In our current times, when somebody uses the term "Florida Cracker" or refers to someone by describing them as a "Real Florida Cracker", they are generally referring to a native-born Floridian, a person both woods and water wise, lives in the country, works outdoors, drives a pick-up truck, hunts and fishes and most certainly has an independent attitude.

An individual that you can bet has a good sharp knife handy on 'em somewhere and can shoot most any type of gun.

A person that can skin a deer and cut 'em up to eat, scale a bream, set a trotline or bush hooks, peel the hide off a catfish, pick birds or dress a gopher. Somebody that might know how to cut the cabbage out of a young palm tree and boil it up, how to catch mullet with a net, split the red-roe out of it, even cleaning and saving the fish's gizzard to eat.

A Cracker can set traps for coons, possums, gators, he can even catch fish in traps in the rivers.

A Cracker can grow a garden and take the produce from it and match it up with any of the afore mentioned food items that he's caught, raised or killed, and make 'em taste good too, cause he can cook, and usually likes to.

Fried mullet.
Fried tenderloin and backstrap (deer or hog).
Fried Bream, Catfish and Bass.
Fried Chicken.
Fried Okra, Squash, Onion.
Fried Turtle (streaked head, softshell, gopher).
Fried Birds (turkey, doves, ducks, quail).
Fried Anything.

A Cracker can Bar-b-que and smoke meats and fish and he's got to have his grits and likes to sweeten things with cane syrup.

A Cracker doesn't mind being alone on hunting or fishing trips, or working alone, sometimes he prefers it. Solitude never bothers a Cracker.

But I've been talking about the "New Florida Cracker". We've retained some of the abilities of the "Old Florida Cracker" to "live off the land" and "make do with what we've got".

Now let me tell you what I think I know about the real "Florida Cracker" and where the name came from and who the people were that earned that distinction.

"Florida Cracker Cowboy" was the full original name that described a man and his job.

Cattle were his business and these were wild free-range cows that roamed and wandered the swamp edges and the big pine and palmetto flats that covered the northern and middle part of the state in the late 1800's and early 1900's.

And the cows had to be hunted, gathered, branded, treated for screwworms, counted, eventually herded up and sold.

And they were scattered for miles in the vast Florida woods.

The Cracker Cowboy rode a horse all day, every day, most carried rifles in scabbards on the saddle, wore wide-brimmed hats, carried leather whips, had trained cow-dogs that could smell-out and catch a cow by his nose and make 'em stand still so the cowboy could get a rope on 'em.

When the dogs had caught a cow or the cowboy had located a bunch of cows or he needed help of any kind he could communicate to the other cowboys, scattered out over a wide area huntin' cows, by the cracking of their whips, which were frayed or braided to the Cracker's own specifications to make it "crack" like he wanted, louder than a rifle shot.

The Crackers had signals worked out, two "cracks"

means this, four "cracks" means that, etc., etc. They cracked those whips driving cattle, literally "popping" those cows out of the woods, making 'em join the rest of the herd and go in the direction they need 'em to go in. They cracked 'em at lazy mules or oxen, theiving stray dogs, rattlesnake heads and troublesome people. The whip was a tool, a weapon and a means of communication.

The sounds of those "Cracker Cowboys", working the swamps and the woods, talking to each other with their whips gave rise to the name of "Florida Cracker".

Those "Crackers" had to be woodsmen, they had to be self-sufficient cause they didn't go home at night or home for weeks or months, wherever the cows lead 'em. "Making do" with what the land provided like swamp cabbage, wild onion, fish and game, gator meat, the much prized gopher turtle, that could be made into the most delicious stew or fried, and the live gophers could be stored in a pen or a pit for weeks without food or water and be available as fresh meat when the need arose.

The Florida Cracker Cowboy was tough, doctoring his cows, his horse and himself, fighting the heat, the bugs, the varmints, the land itself sometimes. They were the explorers and settlers of the "Old Wild Florida", able to take a horse, a rifle, a knife and carve a living off of what the land gave them.

So if somebody calls you a "Cracker", stand tall, look 'em in the eye and say "Thank you," cause they have linked you with a part of our true Florida Heritage that you can be proud of.

South Georgia Settlers

One of my great friends, who I shall call Mr. White, was born and raised in the area west of Coolidge, Georgia, north of Thomasville. He has been kind enough to share some of his family history with me.

The White family settled just west of the "present" town of Coolidge, cause when they decided to farm and build a home on land that bordered the head waters of the Ochlockonee River, there was no town of Coolidge. They had come from North Carolina in a wagon drawn by mules and the year was 1821.

There were four people in the family, a mother and her two grown sons and the older son's wife.

They immediately began clearing land and building a cabin. Winter came before they could get the cabin built and they had to live in the wagon and in a pine-bark shelter..

It was a cold hard winter.

Mr. White's great-great-great grandmother died that winter. Sickness took her.

She's buried near the house Mr. White still lives in and it's now the year 2004.

Mr. White loves his family history and admires and respects the toughness, the bravery, the tenacity and the hard-work ethic it took to clear, build and maintain a farm and to grow, catch, kill, clean and cook the food to sustain themselves.

Of the two brothers that came down with the family in 1821, one was married.

One was not.

One brother was lonely and one was not.

And with their mother dying that first cold winter it was especially hard on the younger unmarried one.

When spring came in the year 1822, the young single brother decided he was returning home to North

Carolina, to civilization and people.

Goodbyes were said.

Tears were shed.

The unmarried brother mounted his mule and left, headed North, to write if he could and try to find a messenger headed to the area. There was no mail service, no post offices.

He was never seen or heard from again.

He didn't make it home or anywhere that he could be found.

Killed by Indians most likely, or vagabonds or thieves, or an accident or illness when he was caught out alone.

But he disappeared off the face of the earth, not found or heard from to this day.

That's the kind of times it was back then. You are on your own, no communication, no calls for help, just oblivion if you're not careful; or even if you are careful.

Mr. White's got a copy of his great-great grandfather's pension papers for fighting in the Indian Wars with Andrew Jackson. I didn't even know they paid pensions back then.

Mr. White told me about a drought he lived through when he was a boy on the farm. How most everybody's wells went dry, and all the creeks and rivers stopped running. He was nine or ten at the time and assigned the task of hauling water to the house on a daily basis. Water that had to come from a well about a half-mile away, dug in a low place next to a farm house that had been abandoned years before when the family moved away. This well held a limited amount of water because the people weren't there to use it.

Anyway, at ten years old he would have to get the mule from the barn, and hitch 'em up to a flat wooden sled with wooden runners. That sled had an oak barrel mounted in the middle of it. He would drive the mule to the abandoned well, draw the water up from the well, a bucket at the time, and fill the barrel. After the barrel was full he'd place a piece of cheesecloth over the top and put an iron hoop over it to hold it on so the water wouldn't slop out. Then he would drive the mule back to the house, unhitch 'em from the sled and put 'em in the barn. Now he could start the normal chores like shucking corn to feed cows, mules, horses, hogs and chickens.

Every day, day in and day out, he'd haul water, till the drought ended.

Mr. White tells me that to this day, our modern times with water at our disposal everywhere, he cannot allow himself to waste one unnecessary cup of water. He tells me that when he brushes his teeth he doesn't run water in the sink and gets just enough in a cup to rinse his mouth out. When he takes a shower he turns on the water, gets himself wet and turns the water off, soaps himself up good and scrubs. Then he turns the water back on to rinse and then off again.

Mr. White knows there's plenty of water on tap but he just can't bear to waste it.

That's how hard an impression that drought put on him, and you know, really he's right. We waste a lot of water that we're probably going to regret one day.

Mr. White and I had a common experience in that both of our mothers died within a week or so of each other.

Mr. White's mother was ninety-one years old and my mother was seventy.

Mr. White was seventy-three and I was fifty-one.

He was as devastated and sorrowful at the loss of his mother as I was at the loss of mine. Me thinking that older-age would make the death of one's mother more easy and understood, more acceptable.

But I learned, that is not true.

It's never any easier no matter what the age, especially when there is so much love and respect involved.

A few months after our mothers had died Mr. White and I were looking over a piece of property. We were standing out in the late afternoon bright August sunshine. There is not a breath of a breeze and sweat's dripping off our noses onto the map of the property we have spread out on the trunk of the car.

We both decide to hunt shade for a minute, fanning ourselves, looking for a breeze anywhere.

We're both commenting on how hot it is.

Mr. White stops and looks me in the eye, sincere and meaningful, and says, "I wish I could have done more for my mother," then he gazes off into the pine trees and is lost in thought for a moment, focused on something in the past.

"I just wish I could have done more," he says again, still looking at something in the beyond.

Well I knew that Mr. White had spent a lot of time and effort in the care of his mother in her later years, and all thru her life. And was still helping in managing the needs of his mother's sisters, (his aunts), that range in age from eighty-six to ninety-five.

So I respond to his statement by saying, "Mr. White you were a good son, you did all you could taking care of your mother the way you did."

And he stopped my response with a raised hand and the shake of his head.

"I mean when I was young, a boy, and my mother was a young woman on the farm." "You think we're hot," he says, "can you imagine how hot it must have been for my mother, to cook three meals a day over a wood-burning cast iron stove, inside an already summertime hot house, with no electricity. And she was sometimes cooking for a lot of people, neighbors who came to "trade" work, planting and harvesting the crops." "She heated cast iron flat-irons on that stove, neatly ironing our families' clothes that she had washed in a cast-iron wash pot set over an open fire in the yard, and scrubbed those clothes on a scrub-board."

It made me stop and think.

About those times and the people and what they had to endure and how hard they had to work just to eat.

I was told about a time of sickness in Mr. White's great-grandparents' time. All three children became gravely ill, from a flu, a virus, an unknown untreatable assailant.

One of the children died and while the parents were attending the funeral of that child, word was sent to the graveyard that another child had died.

This all makes me think about how easy we've all got it, and how spoiled we all are and how trivial a lot of the things that people whine and complain about truly are.

I learned about some of the methods they used to "harvest" fish from the river when Mr. White was growing up. Fish were necessary, important and a welcome part of the family's food. Bass, bream of all kinds, Pike, Jack and Red Horse Suckers were the main targets.

They'd make torches with lighter wood splinters and they'd make special fish-striking irons, that were about three feet long out of old cross-cut saws or flat iron springs that were heated in a charcoal forge and shaped thin on the whacking side, like a thick yardstick or an axle spring that would slice into water with less resistance than something flat or round.

On dark nights they'd shine those fish laying in shallow pools and whack 'em in the head and have a fine supper.

On bright sunshine days they'd lay water-soaked logs, that wouldn't float, in the shallow water between deep holes and sprinkle white sand on the log. Then they would climb up in a tree where they could see down on the log and could spot big bass and jack when they swam across the white sand. This enabled 'em to take a .30-.30 rifle and shoot those fish for dinner.

They made fish traps out of chicken wire and placed 'em with the funnel, or the entry point of the trap facing down-stream. When the "Red-Bellies" migrated upstream to spawn they would swim in the trap and keep on swimming, facing the current and never even think about turning around and getting out, cause that would mean swimming downstream, and a "Red-Belly" ain't trained to do that during spawning season.

Those traps could be checked and emptied regular and always have a good mess of bream in the spring time.

All the regular methods of fishing, trotlines, bush-hooks, cane poles baited with earthworms, crickets, grasshoppers, grubs or chicken guts were employed too.

The .22 rifle was a good provider for farm families. Squirrels, rabbits, fish in the shallow water, turkeys or anything that would stand still long enough to get a bullet into that you could eat.

Hog-killing time was a period of long hard work on a cold winter's day cause there was no refrigeration, but some great eating was coming on. Fresh fried tenderloin, smoke-house sausage and hams, souse-meat, head-cheese, brains and eggs, chittlins if you cared for them. With no refrigeration other than the winter air, the meat had to be salt-cured or smoked in the smoke-house over hickory or oak fires to preserve it.

Lotsa wild game supplemented the meat part of the diet, deer-meat, turkey, wild hogs, quail were a special treat.

Garden vegetables, raised on the farm, made up the rest of the fare. Turnip and collard greens, peas of all types, beans, new potatoes, sweet potatoes, tomatoes, cucumbers, corn, okra, squash, watermelon. Most items had to be "canned" for use in the winter. A lot of people "grew syrup" or raised sugar cane to make cane syrup out of. It was used for sweetening everything from pies, to biscuits, to tea. Peanut brittle was made with it from peanuts grown on the farm.

Peanuts were grown for the oil, for people food and for hog food.

Milk came from a cow each morning.

Mr. White told me what a marvel it was when the first tractor came along with a peanut-picker type of attachment that would separate the hand-stacked and dried peanut vines from the nuts, and then the hay press would bale up the peanut vines into hay. The tractor he first saw had iron wheels and could do in a day what it took hand-labor a week to do.

Most of this way of life sounds really good till you think about what they didn't have.

No electricity.

No telephone.

No lights, T.V., or radio.

No running water.

No heat other than the wood burning fireplace and cook stove.

No medical, life, health, fire, disease, dental or disaster insurance.

No food insurance either, no food stamp program or welfare of any kind.

We all need to know and remember what life was like just a short time ago.

We need to think about and remember how comforted and medicated, well fed and educated, and fortunate we all are to live like we do.

Remember the White family of South Georgia and the thousands of families like them that settled our part of the world when it was wild and untamed. That learned and progressed and respected the family and the country, and the values of the work ethic it took to survive and prosper. These people recognized the opportunity afforded to all of us if we will work hard, be imaginative, be loyal to our families and their good values, stand up for what is right and at the very least work hard enough to sustain yourself and your family instead of relying on others to take care of you as seems to be so rampant in our society today.

Think back to what your parents, grandparents and great-grandparents had or didn't have.

Think about what you have or could of had.

Think about what you could have done, or can do, to make things better for you and yours.

History is a great teacher of the present and the future.

Those South Georgia settlers could teach us all a lot, and those that grew up paying attention have had full, successful lives.

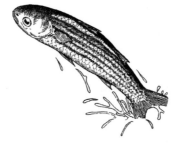

QUAIL   CLAY MARSHALL LOVEL
04

Quail

We had a lot of quail running wild around where I grew up. You could hear 'em whistling and calling in the evenings.

They scared the stew out of us a bunch of times when we'd be playing in the woods and fields, them exploding under our feet with a sound and motion that vibrated your whole body and mind with that whirring and beating of wings, an unearthly sound of a covey of twenty or thirty bob-white quail, taking off wide-open from a standing start 360 degrees around you.

We'd see 'em all the time.

In the garden, pecking around the edges.

Crossing the yard or the dirt road in front of our house.

They were fun to watch when they would decide to cross a road or a clear place in the woods.

The covey would sort of ooze up to the edge of the road where the weeds and grass still gave 'em some cover. They'd sort of pile-up in a crowd like people do at a good movie when the ticket window opens.

Then one quail would bolt across the bare dirt road to the safety of the weeds on the other side. That quail would be standing straight-up and erect when he ran across the road, but his feet would be invisible cause they were moving so fast. He'd cross that road in the blink of an eye and as soon as he'd hit the weeds and cover on the other side he'd stop as quick as he started and go back to his slow, peck-peck jerky cadence with no concerns.

Two more birds would dart across the road in the same hectic manner.

Then another one would cross.

Then the rest of the covey would flow across the road in the same frantic, speed-of-light, running-for-your-life manner to join the rest of the group.

A full minute would pass.

Then a late, scaredy-cat quail would run across like the rest except even faster and zig-zagging, maybe even chirping as he runs calling for the rest of the birds to wait, him being left behind and frightened.

They are beautiful and hilarious to watch.

They are absolutely delicious to eat and our family of five rarely got to eat quail cause we never had enough to feed everybody.

I finally found a way to kill enough quail for us all to eat, but to get the amount of birds I needed, I had to be invited dove hunting first.

Here's how dove hunting is related to quail killing.

About every other Sunday I'd get invited to go to Uncle Thomas' farm near Quincy and hunt doves.

If we made it home from church in time I'd grab my ole 410 bolt-action shotgun, my hunting hat and vest, and run to the neighbors house. They'd load four or five of us boys in the back seat, our shotguns in the trunk, and drive us to Uncle Thomas' corn field and dump us out.

Usually they put us young boys in the worst part of the field, where there wasn't many birds flying by to shoot at, the adults keeping the best-shooting places to themselves.

I'd have lots of time to kill waiting for a bird to fly by close enough to shoot at. Sometimes I'd shoot at one not close enough to shoot at, just to shoot, but I didn't do this often cause shotgun shells were scarce and expensive.

Anyway back to the quail story.

Uncle Thomas' field had dried ears of corn laying and hanging everywhere. To fill all this spare time I had I'd be watching the sky, shelling an ear of corn, breaking each golden kernel off the milk-white cob, chewing on a piece or two just for something to do.

I'd fill my mostly-empty game bag full of shelled corn, fill my pockets up too. I had a plan that would help us eat a few more quail dinners.

I wouldn't have but maybe a dove or two when we came home from Uncle Thomas' farm, but I'd have my limit in quail bait.

There was a big briar patch down from the house, it had lots of blackberries in the summer and a big covey of quail hung around it most all the time.

I crawled in that briar patch and laid me a nice neat line of shelled corn, putting plenty of it, making a bright yellow stripe ending where the briars quit.

After school the next day I go check and see if I had any "customers", eating my corn. I wouldn't even have to look to see if the birds were partaking of my bait. I could sneak up real quiet and hear birds chirping softly, their multitudes of little quail feet making crackly noises in the leaves.

I'd run home and come back with my trusty 410 with one shell in the chamber and two more in the magazine.

I'd crawl slow and quiet to a position that looks right down my corn-line. I can hear all the birds peeping and rustling around.

I'm on my belly, holding that bolt-action 410 at quail height aiming it right down the corn-line, looking over the barrel at a dozen or more fat quail standing on both sides of that yellow stripe filling their bellies.

They are lined-up just right as I slip the safety off and pull the trigger.

Quail explode everywhere.

I'm up on my knees now, jacking another shell into the chamber and getting another shot off into the cloud of brown and white feathers that's blasting off through the trees.

A bird falls from the air and I bolt after 'em and pick 'em up.

Now I go back to check the corn-line.

Hotdog it's quail for everybody! There's four birds shot dead, one more flopping around that I have to chase and wring its neck. That's five off the corn-line, one I shot flying for a total of six birds giving us one extra.

Those quail sure tasted good the next night with rice and gravy.

Corn-line shooting quail is a much more efficient way to bag birds than banging away at 'em flying in the air. It makes your bird to shotgun shell ratio go way up too.

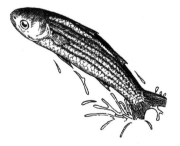

Wood Ducks

Anybody that ever hunted Wooducks in the late evening has never killed any that were legal.

Evidently the birds have watches on their little feathered legs, that tell them the exact minute after legal shooting hours. You can't even trick those wily birds when it changes to Daylite Savings Time, they still wait till dark.

I remember one time when I was thirteen or fourteen years old, we had located a huge bunch of wooducks roosting in the east end of Fords Arm, a branch off of Lake Jackson.

We had been bream fishing at dark and seen all those ducks come piling in. We made plans to come back and shoot some the next evening.

Butch and John and I met up in the woods on the shoreline of the lake where we kept an old leaky wood boat that had to be bailed constantly. We had one broke paddle, a four-foot two-by-four and a long stick for power. We pushed and paddled our way across the open water of Fords Arm into a grass and tree-filled swampy part of the lake, where those wooducks liked to roost.

Butch and John put me off on a little dry tussock of land that has built up around a couple of old Gum trees and they paddled off and hid in the boat about seventy-five yards away.

We know we're a little early cause the setting sun is just now touching the tops of the trees on the horizon.

You wouldn't think there was a duck in the world right now. There's no birds flying anywhere, nothing but water, trees, moss and weeds.

But you know what's going to happen when it starts to get dark.

The sun's down now. The sky is pinky-orange to the west, over head the sky is a dark grey-blue, back to the east it's getting dark enough for a star or two to shine out.

Suddenly you hear the whistling of wings, glimpse the black silhouettes of ducks darting and weaving through the trees, hear the splash as they light on the water and hear 'em peeping and calling to their brethren that are coming in behind 'em.

And boy do they come. One wad after the other, two to twenty birds to the group, the sound is constant now of wing split-wind and calling birds.

Now the sound of twelve gauge shotguns join in the mix, mine, John's and Butch's. You can see the flame of the burning powder come out the barrel when Butch or John shoot cause it's the getting so dark. I'm sure they can see the flames coming out of mine cause I'm shooting, reloading and shooting some more with that old 870. Or at least I'm trying to shoot. There's so many ducks and they're coming by so fast and close that half the time that you try to shoot one you can't even catch up with 'em to pull the trigger.

The best tactic is to ignore those birds that are almost blowing your hat off as they zoom by and pick you a spot over head that has a little blue-grey sky behind it and shoot at the coal-black flying specks that cross it.

It's wide open now, shoot, load, shoot, shoot again. You know you're putting some down when you hear 'em crash into the water.

Now we notice headlites on the hillside that comes down to the lake on the far side, we can hear car doors slam, see flashlites winking around.

We're still firing occasionally, the flame out the end of the barrel looks six-feet long it's getting so dark.

We can hear some one pulling on a crank-cord, trying to start an outboard motor, it sputtering and cutting off.

I can hear Butch and John pushing and paddling, coming to pick me up and they are in a big hurry. When they get to me they're telling me in excited loud whispers that the boat we're hearing is the warden and we got to get out of here.

I'm in the front of the boat slashing at the water with a limb, it's too deep to pole, Butch and John paddling like crazy with the two-by-four and the broken paddle.

We can hear the buzzy bee-like sound of a small outboard breaking out into the open part of the lake, we're about two-thirds of the way across.

I have to break from paddling to bail water out or we'll sink. While I'm bailing and facing back behind us, a flashlite beam flickers across the boat and then comes back and settles on us.

"Hold it right there," somebody yells at us from the boat that's following, "Stop where you are," they shout, centering the flashlite beam on us. The high-pitched whine of that little outboard motor getting louder every second.

The sound of that pursuing outboard jumps up to a real high pitch, and we hear somebody cuss and the flashlite beam comes off us and is shined to the back of the warden's boat, illuminating the officer that's running that rig and he has shut the engine off, has it pulled up, trying to get the weeds off the prop.

That's the break we need.

Butch and John go back to paddling like crazy. I throw my stick away and use the stock of my old shotgun as a paddle and we've got that leaky boat throwing wake behind it as we huff and puff and splash our way to the dark tree line.

We hear the motor crank back up behind us, the flashlite catches us in its glare again and we can hear both officers yelling at us.

We're committed and we ain't looking back or listening. If we can get to those woods we're gone. We had to walk from home to here and we won't mind running back.

The boat's twenty yards behind us and gaining,

we're lit-up by the flashlite like performers on the stage, digging in that water like madmen.

We would have been had if it hadn't been for that good-ole Lake Jackson, bottle-brush looking weed that grows from the bottom to the surface and gets so thick in some places a motor won't run through it.

We hear that outboard motor go to that high-pitched screaming whine as the prop tangles in the weeds choking it down.

We're in wading distance of the shoreline and the dark woods, and we jump out and abandon our leaky getaway craft. The water is way over the tops of our boots but we don't care. We're sloshing and splashing, moving as fast as we can, laughing out loud in our excitement, ignoring the cussing and yelling coming from the boat behind us.

We're on hard ground now, running as hard as we can with our water-filled rubber boots squishing with every step. We break out of the woods onto a graded dirt road that leads home, it's pitch dark now and we think we're home free. We're running in single file fast as we can and we round a sharp bend in the road.

The boy in front stops so fast the other two of us about run 'em over. And the reason he has stopped is because we have nearly run smack into the front bumper of a dark-colored four-door Ford.

They have caught us.

All that effort wasted, all that jubilation at escaping .so short lived.

We sheepishly amble around to the driver's door.

We've give up.

We look in the rolled up windows and see a teenage boy and girl, wrapped up so tight in a long deep kiss that they don't even know we're there.

I know it must of scared that couple when they heard us laughing and yelling and running away again up that old gravel road.

Ain't nobody gonna catch us now and if we hurry we won't even be late for supper.

We returned to check on our boat a few days later and found that the broken paddle and two-by-four were gone along with the two or three shot-up decoys we had that wouldn't float right anyway. There was a big hole knocked in the bottom making it useless.

We weren't even mad.

The old boat was rotten and we would have gladly traded all that we lost for not having to face our Daddy's with a citation from the Game Department.

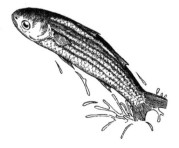

Homemade Reloads

Me and my brother-in-law Bruce ran the bay together, learned to mullet fish together and killed our share of ducks together.

We'd leave out fishing in our mullet skiff and on some winter days when we'd break out into the bay, the bay would be so full of ducks we'd just turn around and go back for the decoys and shotguns.

Forget the fish.

You just couldn't turn the opportunity down.

The grey winter sky would be black with clouds of ducks whizzing in every direction. Thousands jumping up when the oyster boats would change oyster-tonging holes.

We'd run back to the dock, go get our guns, shells and decoys, race that mullet skiff back out to one of the islands off Spring Creek, throw two dozen decoys out and be shootin' ducks before we could get the boat hidden.

I remember shooting my gun empty two or three times just trying to get the decoys out from a mullet skiff that was painted white.

The birds were thick and crazy.

But we just couldn't kill enough of 'em.

Most of 'em were just out of reach for our store-bought shells. Twenty yards out of range from where we had to put the decoys out.

We needed better shells.

Custom-made bullets.

So we ordered a re-loader to make our own shells.

And we had a friend that made and tested gun-powder at a local factory, he told us what we needed to get for maximum speed and range.

We ordered that too.

And the reloader came.

And we unpacked it, assembled it and threw the directions away without a glance.

We knew what we wanted.

We wanted the most powder and the most shot we could pack in a 2 3/4", twelve-gauge hull.

So the little silver sleeves that came with the reloader, (the sleeves that measure the power and shot, that are supposed to go into the slide-bars on the reloader), went into the trash.

Our first reloaded shells didn't seem to want to crimp shut on the ends. We'd just mash and mash with the reloader till they almost closed. Thinking they wouldn't look as pretty as store-bought shells anyway, we decided they were o.k.

Some of the shot would spill out the ends of the shells but not much, (we had a good amount packed in), way too much as it turned out and way too much hot powder too.

We finally got two or three boxes loaded and were ready for the next morning of duck-hunting at daylite.

We are out there early. Decoys set in the same ole place, us hiding in the bushes, loaded up with our custom-made, high powered souped-up duck loads.

Me with my 870 pump and Bruce with his trusty double-barrel, both 12 gauge guns.

Here comes the first flight of Scaulp, braking and gliding at forty-miles-an-hour into the decoys.

We both throw our guns to our shoulders, take aim and cut loose.

I shoot my three shells and Bruce shoots his two.

Ducks folded and fell like rain, just like we had envisioned and we looked at each other and smiled.

And Bruce told me I had blood running down from my mouth, as he rubbed his right shoulder.

And I had a shell lodged in the chamber and couldn't get it out. The brass part of the casing was bent concave into the chamber area of my old pump gun.

Must be part of the problem of using reloads, I thought, as I took a stick and pushed the bent-spent empty shell out of the barrel.

We're both reloading as fast as we can cause more ducks are coming in and we've got the right stuff now to work 'em over.

We fire all we've got at the next bunch and there are ducks laying all over the water.

I'm cussing now cause my shoulder, (from the recoil), feels like it's been crushed and Bruce is saying his side-by-side is tore-up cause he just pulled one trigger and it's firing both barrels at the same time.

But we're loading up cause there's another bunch on its way in and there must be thirty ducks in that group.

Bam, Bam, Boom.

Ducks are falling, we're moaning and groaning from the recoil, and the bottom pointy-part of the stock on Bruce's double-barrel has broken and fallen off.

I've got another empty shell, bent and lodged in the chamber of my 870 and can't pry it out.

And I'm really in no hurry, cause my shoulder hurts so bad.

Bruce puts the piece of broken gun-stock in his pocket and reloads, wondering what's wrong with his gun, it firing both barrels every time at the same time and I finally get the jammed shell out and reload too.

Here the ducks come again, like you dream about, as fast as you can reload another bunch is pitching in to the decoys.

We cut loose again but it's a real short volley.

Bruce's shotgun fires both barrels at the same time again.

I only get one shot before the empty shell is sucked up the barrel not letting me chamber another round and my lip is swollen and bleeding and we're both cussing and rubbing our shoulders in bad pain like we'd been hit by a truck.

Besides that we've got more ducks floating off in the tide-current than is allowed, our guns are broke, (Bruce's fore-grip under the barrel has fallen off this time), my gun is unjammable and I've suffered enough.

Damn these shells are good!

Our guns must be wore-out.

We found out later that we were lucky to be alive.

Those must have been damn good guns to hold together with the amounts of explosives we'd packed in 'em.

Our friend in the gun powder business came in to eat at the restaurant and I mentioned how good the shells were but that our guns were tore-up and the shells wouldn't crimp shut tight and we were both somewhat injured.

He inspected our reloading equipment, saw that we had thrown the measuring sleeves away, told us how lucky we were that we hadn't blown ourselves up. He dug the instruction sheet out of the trash can, handed it to us and walked away, shaking his head.

We've never had shells again as good as those were, but we haven't had anymore gun trouble and we hadn't blown ourselves up either.

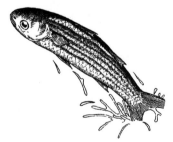

Miss Lib

Miss Lib was Hubert's wife and they operated Spring Creek Marina that rented wooden skiffs and sold bait and tackle. As hard a working person as you'll ever know, and a kinder happier person you'll never meet.

But she could get tough when she needed to. Busting Bert in the mouth with her strong right hand when he was drunk and cussed her.

Hubert Hinton's an amazing man. One leg gone at the hip, one arm off at the shoulder. Electrocuted back in the 50's working on a power line. He didn't let that mishap set 'em back too much though, cause he learned to do more with one arm and one leg than most people can do with all their limbs. Hunt, fish, repair outboard motors, do electrical work, pull an anchor, anything but run too fast he can do.

Anyway Hubert and Lib had gone to bed after a long day renting boats, fixing motors, selling bait. They went to sleep but Miss Lib woke up about one a.m. and couldn't go back to sleep so she was slowly pacing around the dark house, occasionally staring out the window.

Directly across the driveway from Miss Lib's window are parked a row of fourteen to sixteen foot boats on trailers, all with little nine to fifteen horse outboards clamped on the back, and lo-and-behold there's two men, quietly unscrewing the clamps and lifting the little outboard off the stern and walking back to their car and putting it in the trunk.

And they walk back to another boat and start taking the motor off of it.

Miss Lib's already gone and shaken Hubert quietly awake, whispering to 'em what's going on.

Now it takes Hubert a few minutes to get mobile when he's getting out of bed, cause he's got to get his leg strapped on before he can walk and he's got a little chair with wheels on it he can sit and roll around on to fetch his leg and put it on.

Miss Lib's peeking out the window and whispering to Hubert that they've about got the motor off and they're going to get away, before they can stop 'em.

Hubert's got his pistol out of the drawer trying to get his leg strapped on, quietly cussing under his breath, trying to hurry.

Miss Lib picks up her B.B. gun that she's got leaning against the wall in the kitchen, the one she uses to sting the tomcats that yowl in the night chasing her sweet kitty.

The thieves have gotten the second motor loose and are lifting it off the boat when Miss Lib charges out the door into the black night, B.B. gun leading the way, up to her should and ready to fire as she runs up to the would be thieves commanding them to freeze and drop that outboard.

The thieves are stunned that they've been caught and an enraged woman is pointing a shotgun with a big fat black barrel in their faces, threatening to shoot 'em if they move.

Hubert's called the sheriff and has now rolled his chair up to the doorway where he's got his leg in his lap, his pistol in his hand and he's screaming at Lib to kill 'em if they move a muscle, kill 'em anyway if she wants to, and wait till he gets his leg on and he'll kill 'em for her.

The thieves are frozen in fright, they are drunk as it turned out and now some man is begging his wife to shoot 'em.

They are on their knees begging for her not to kill 'em, Miss Lib keeping 'em both covered with the barrel of her Daisy.

Those bad boys never moved till the sheriff got there, they were glad when the sheriff got there cause Hubert had finally got his leg on and was headed their way pointing his pistol and reading the riot act to 'em as he approached.

Miss Lib got a special citation from the Sheriff's department.

It takes a brave, strong woman to apprehend two stealing men in the dark with a B.B. gun.

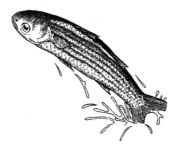

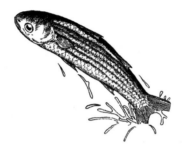

Hunting and Stalking a Man

Hunting is when usually you're laying up, waiting on your prey and stalking is when you've spotted the prey, (or thief as this turned out to be) and are trying to slip up on it.

This is the first time for me a man has been on the other end of this hunt, rather than a deer or turkey or fish, but hunting is what it was, boiled down to it.

I had finished closing down the restaurant and locking it up. Was putting some pieces of chocolate peanut butter pie in my truck, fixing to go home. It was about 10 p.m., quiet and dark in Spring Creek, I was bushed from a day on the ACE, stone crabbing.

I'm starting to get in my truck when I notice an old, Olds Cutlass, turn off the paved road onto Oak Street, which is dirt, coast past the only street lite in town and ease to a stop in the dark shadows of a Live Oak tree.

Not real unusual.

People tend to get lost down here sometimes, us being at the end of a dead-end road.

But this was different.

Soon as the car came to a complete stop a man got out of the passenger side, lit-up for a second by the interior lites.

Quick as he could close the door the old Olds did a three-point-turn and left the area quicker than he had come in.

I was now interested.

Specially since I'd seen the man was dressed from head to toe in camouflage and was now slipping thru the black-dark shadows, like a coon or a cat, heading straight to our small marina where we keep all our boats and gear.

There's eight or ten flats-fishing boats with rods, reels, motors, gas tanks, all the inshore gear, there's also five or six mullet skiffs, loaded with all the tools to catch fish.

And then there's the ACE, tied-up down there too. That old wood and glass workhorse, thirty-two feet long and diesel powered, a boat we did everything with.

A boat I had a pile of time, money and emotion in.

A boat that I'd spent the last twelve hours on pulling stone crab traps, dumping the crabs, breaking the claws, bustin' my butt, cold and wet all day long.

After crabbing all day, I'd come back in and cooked the claws, graded 'em out, packed 'em, cleaned the cooking room and worked two hours in the restaurant till closing time.

Anyway.

I'm suspicious, so I get my pistol, an old thirty-two I carried around, hadn't been fired in five or six years, a cheap gun.

I walk the hundred yards or so thru the dark to the marina.

Ease up to the old white heart-pine cracker house that sits on the canal bank and peek around the corner.

The camoed stranger is just reaching the part of the dock where the ACE is tied up.

There's two big fiberglass ice boxes sitting end to end on the dock, boxes that will hold eight hundred pounds each, that we take off the back deck of the ACE when we go stone crabbing.

Camo-man is just reaching those iceboxes when he either hears something or senses my presence.

Camo-man lays down flat and quickly crawls behind that wall of iceboxes.

He's outta sight, completely disappearing from my vision.

I'm real interested now.

You might say my curiosity is peeked.

I just sit down behind that old house, ease half an eyeball around the corner and watch the boxes stacked on the dock where I think I saw camo-man lay down and hide.

I'm still-hunting now, just watching and waiting, nothing to see, nothing to hear.

Then I see 'em.

He's just peeked his head out from the bottom side of the iceboxes, checking everything out like an old box-turtle will do before he makes his move.

Draws his head back in like an ole turtle does too.

I just sit still, lookin', waiting.

Old camo-turtleman sticks his head out again.

Long look and study of the area this time, really checking it out.

Head goes back in and he stands up, looks around one more time then hops on the ACE. I can hear his feet hit the deck cause it's low-tide and a pretty good jump down.

That was the wrong thing to do.

I thought I smelled a rat.

I thought there might be something wrong about this.

Now I know without a doubt that this was severe mischief-in-progress.

And I was totally tired, instantly mad, insulted and pissed-off.

Those iceboxes camo-turtleman had hid behind worked against 'em now.

I eased out on quiet green grass that runs down to the dock, I'm in a crouch, on my toes moving quick, keeping those iceboxes lined-up to block my view from the ACE and camo-turtleman till I could get up behind them.

I am now stalking a man.

And from this position, hidden by the iceboxes I can look down on the milky-white, night shadowed, totally cleared-off deck of the ACE.

And there's ole camo-turtle-thief-man.

His back's to me.

He's busy.

He's completely focused and intent on opening the bulkhead doors to the cabin of the boat.

That does it.

Around the iceboxes I come, cross the dock and jump the five feet to the deck, landing two feet behind the culprit.

Camo-turtleman is turning around from the sound.

I'm lunging toward 'em, closing fast.

By the time the would-be thief is fully faced toward me I've got ahold of his collar and have shoved the four-inch barrel of that thirty-two caliber pistol as far in his neck, as a tired, wore-out, thoroughly mad, exited old stone-crabber could shove it.

I had camo-turtleman's total attention and obedience.

"What are you doing and who are you?" I growl and hiss in his face, almost lost in my madness and tiredness.

"I'm so and so and such and such," he gurgles back, "son of so and so," he squeaks.

"What are you doing here?" I say again, noticing his totally unfamiliar face and the teardrop tattoo at the corner of his eye, shoving that pistol harder till the cylinder is disappearing under his jaw.

"I been set-up, set-up," he croaks out, having trouble speaking.

I think he had some steel in his throat or something.

"I left my clothes on this boat when we went fishing today," he lies to me.

This really gets me upset after what I been through on "this boat" today.

But I'm trying to stay calm and doing a good job cause I hadn't shot 'em yet.

Next thing I know we're headed up the long dock,

the one bordering the side of the canal with all our mullet skiffs and hook and line trout boats tied up in a row like racehorses at the starting gate.

I've got camo-turtleman hugged-up tight, collar in one hand, pistol-in-his-neck in the other.

I'm telling 'em what a no-good thieving sorry so and so he is and he's begging me not to kill 'em.

I'm marching 'em up the dock, by the rows of tied-up boats when we come to the only empty slip. The tide's way down, five or six feet to the water from the dock's edge.

I'm cussing, he's begging and somehow (we've never known how), but somehow ole camo-landturtleman, becomes camo-waterturtleman and goes flying off the dock, screaming as he goes and luckily lands in the water, instead of landing in a boat which probably would have killed 'em.

Before he hits the water I'm screaming for him to "get out", "get out before I shoot you".

He's begging me not to shoot.

I'm still hollering, "Get out of the water, GET OUT, GET OUT."

I'm yelling, he's blubbering, bubbling, splashing and begging. His hand reaches out and I grab it and I drag 'em over the dock where he lays gasping like a fish outta water.

"Get up, get up," I'm growling and marching 'em again up towards the restaurant and the phone to call the law and lock 'em up.

Then I realize I've go not real charges other than trespassing against 'em cause I didn't let 'em steal anything.

That really pisses me off.

So I kick 'em in the ass as hard as I can and shove 'em away telling him to get his sorry no-good, stealing-thieving self away from here or next time I'll hurt 'em.

He staggers and wanders his way up the road outta

sight.

I call the sheriff's department, give 'em his name and they tell me they'll check it out.

And that's the end of the story till a few days later.

Come to find out that after I'd kicked camo-man up the road, he had gone about a block, broke into an empty house, ate their food, stole some dry clothes and spent the night.

The next day he must of have worked his way up toward Crawfordville cause that's where he commits his next foul deed.

One of my restaurant customers, that's in the construction business, told me this story.

He told me he was on his way to pick up his brother to go to work. It's just before daylite early in the morning.

A block or so from his brother's house he notices a man walking down the road carrying a big radio and a lot of other stuff wrapped in his arms.

Not a real unusual sight but sorta curious.

A few minutes later he's banging on his brother's door trying to wake 'em up, thinking he has overslept again.

Trying the door and finding it open he goes in his brother's bedroom to find him bloody and just regaining consciousness, propped up in his bed.

The bloody brother tells the just arriving brother that when his alarm clock went off he sat up in bed, reaching over to turn his alarm off. Just as his hand reached the clock he glimpses something moving out of the corner of his eye and looks up in time to see a man swing a baseball bat upside his head, luckily just knocking him out and back into bed.

The healthy brother calls an ambulance and the sheriff's office, giving comfort and aid to his wounded brother. Concern, bewilderment, shock and rage come rushing to his mind all at once.

And a recent memory.

The recollection of a man walking down the road, away from his wounded brother's house with a radio and an arm load of stuff.

Curiosity, suspiciousness, realization.

It's him, the one who did it, the one who smacked his brother in the head with a ball bat.

"Help's coming brother, lay back till the ambulance gets here, it'll be awright," healthy brother says as he's moving toward the door. "I be right back," and now he's running toward his truck.

Back up the road he goes, spinning his tires, shifting gears hard, retracing his path and he's jaw-clenching mad.

And there he is, not far from where he'd passed 'em a little earlier, the same man.

Just walking along, carrying his wounded brother's radio and the other stuff he'd stolen, making time for somewhere.

Healthy-furious brother slams brakes beside, (would you believe it?) camo-turtleman, jumping out of his truck before it stops moving, screaming thief related adjectives and attacks. He knocks camo-turtleman, stealing man, heartless-man, beneath-a-snake's-belly man, two times in prison already man, to the ground and beats 'em senseless before he knows what's happened.

(Side note: the tattooed tear-drop at the corner of the eye is the inmate's badge of honor for serving five years in the pen)

The deputies take camo-turtleman thief to jail.

The wounded brother recovers.

A year later ole camo-turtleman tries to press charges against me for assault, while he's in jail waiting to be sentenced again, at the expense of the county and state, using free attorneys.

Expensive stuff.

Just think of the misery, the loss, the human suffering

and expense to the hardworking taxpayers that would have been saved if I'd just shot ole camo-turtleman on the ACE and baited up my traps with 'em.

I don't think even crabs will eat anything that sorry and rotten.

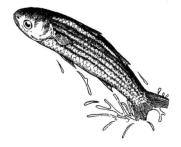

Slicker Suit

Other than the boat, your slicker was the most important piece of equipment you owned.

I've always said that I'd like to write a book and title it "My Life in a Rubber Suit" cause I spent a lot of time in my life fishing, or cleaning fish, or pulling crab traps, and my slicker suit was my second skin.

Helly Hansen or Grundens was the brand I wore. Heavy rubber-plastic slicker-pants, with adjustable elastic suspenders that clipped on the front and back, your body covered in a protective sheath from chest to your feet.

Paired with a good set of rubber boots you were basically waterproof from the neck down.

And you never went anywhere without your slicker jacket, usually stuck under the bow of the boat somewhere but always there.

I never left the dock without wearing my slicker-britches, you worked in those all the time, on the water crabbing or fishing it was the same as socks and underwear.

But my moldy-on-the-inside slicker coat was always close at hand.

When the conditions were right that was the most valuable part of the complete slicker suit, and it was priceless.

When the rain or the fog or the wind or the cold or any combination of these factors broke out, that slicker-jacket could seal your whole body off except your face.

Mine were always a dark green, (green or orange was all you could get), a heavy rubberized water-proof coating on the outside. The inside of the pants and the coat were of a white, heavy-woven nylon.

The jacket was long to the waist, double snapped and overlapped to keep the wind and water out down the front where you fastened it up. A waterproof hood with drawstrings was snugged-up around your head and you could have on your Sunday Best, go fishing in a blowing rain Southwester and take off the slicker-suit and go to church.

You could sit on the bow of a mullet skiff while it poured rain, the lightning struck and the wind blew forty knots.

At night.

For hours.

Shoulders hunched, arms laid across your knees, sitting on the bow-cap facing down, so the sheets of water will hit the back of your head, draining down the sides of the hood of your jacket.

I always wore a ball-cap underneath the hood, and the water would be in a constant stream off the brim of the hat, flowing into the bottom of the boat.

You could holler and hoot when a six-foot wave would breach over the side of the ACE when you were pulling stone crab traps. The boat running due north up the trap line and the weather blowing north-east-by-east throwing spray and an occasional solid green wave on top of you.

That slicker would keep you warm and dry where you could bear it.

I've seen steam rising off the backs of Ben and Charlie's slicker-jackets when it was sleeting on a freezing grey day in February.

That was the day our hands took such punishment from the cold and Ben made the statement, "Pop, I think all the glamour has gone out of crabbing."

He was right.

Keep you warm and dry in the winter-time those slickers would.

Burn you like a one-man sauna-suit and keep you soaking wet with sweat in the summer. You never wore the jacket but you had to wear the coverall part to keep the slime, stinging jelly-fish, fish fins and salt water off.

Couldn't have made it without those slickers.

The average sports fisherman could buy a good slicker suit and it would last a lifetime.

A gill-net fisherman could get two or three years out of one if the snaps on the jacket don't corrode to where they tear off.

A crabber pulling wire traps might get six-months without scratching all the water proof rubber off the front, if his belly ain't too big.

Seemed like the first good wet cold-front of the fall, when the roe mullet were starting to run, I was always buying me a new slicker-suit.

Knowing I'd get my money's worth.

Handing down my old set to Ben or Clay and they were glad to have 'em, cause they were young and didn't mind a few leaks here and there.

Baited Field

We worked hard all summer on Charlies' seventeen acre field that sits in front of his pretty home in Gadsden County.

It was grown over thick but we got it mowed then burned and finally harrowed-up clean.

Dove season was about a month away so we got ready and "planted wheat". Now we don't want our wheat to grow like most farmers. We don't even want ours to sprout and we pray it doesn't rain cause that makes the wheat seed sprout and the birds don't like it after that.

I'd been using this process for years, following somewhat normal farming practices. Not scattering new seed over sprouted seed, turning the dirt over and putting out new seed after a rain. The State Game Wardens had checked us many times, standing shoe-sole deep in fresh wheat. Never a problem.

Anyway we had Charlie's field properly planted for birds and what a crop we had coming on. Sam, Charlie's wife, would call me in the evenings and describe the droves and droves of doves flying in to feed.

It was obvious we were going to have a good opening weekend shoot so we planned a big party that evening to fry fresh doves, make rice and gravy, lima beans, sliced tomatoes, the works.

Everything worked as planned. We all shot our limits late that afternoon, plenty of birds. Clay quit early and luckily was reading a book under the house where the cooking was going on. Mr. Rivers, Johnny's dad, hadn't felt well during the heat of the afternoon and elected to go out in the field in the cool of the evening to shoot a few.

Johnny accompanied his father to spot and retrieve his birds, not even taking his gun cause he'd already shot the limit.

Mr. Rivers had just pulled the trigger and shot his first bird when the game wardens pulled up.

Three game wardens.

Three camoed, jack-booted, pistol-belted, radio-hung, surly, unpleasant Federal Game Wardens.

One takes off through the field toward Mr. Rivers, where Johnny has gone off to fetch his daddies downed dove.

The two other wardens approach us at the house where we're picking birds for our feast.

All our parents are there, our children, wives and lots of good friends.

And the wardens are going to bust us for illegal baiting in front of everybody.

We try to argue and ask questions, to no , they won't talk to us, we're basically ignored other than to gather up our licenses and check our shotguns.

Johnny is having a particularly bad time of it with the Fed that's checking he and his Daddy.

First the Warden is trying to charge Johnny with passing game, cause he saw 'em hand the bird he'd retrieved to Mr. Rivers, saying Johnny had over the limit and was giving some away. Then the warden dropped Mr. Rivers' empty game vest on the ground at his feet when he got through checking it.

We had to hold Johnny back from whipping that rude warden when he did that mean trick, and the cussing Johnny gave the agent didn't help our situation.

To make a long story short they charged five of us for shooting over bait.

Worst of all they took all our birds that we had planned on feeding everybody with. Only out of the goodness of their mean little hearts did they not confiscate our lima beans and rice. We had to thaw out some doe meat to fry for supper.

Mr. Leston Rivers, Mr. Johnny Rivers, Mr. Charles

Thomas, Mr. Ben Lovel and Mr. Leo Lovel all received citations in the mail. These citations claimed we were to pay five hundred and fifty dollars a piece for our sins.

Outrageous.

Ridiculous.

Robbery.

And we're innocent anyway.

We're going to court and I tell all the accused not to worry.

I'll represent us and let the judge decide on this.

The extent of my legal training was pretty obvious as soon as our case was called, cause the first thing that Federal Judge asked me to do was to plead either guilty or not guilty.

Well this caught me totally off-guard and my response to the judge was that I had come to court to present my case and let him decide if we were guilty or not guilty.

He quickly told me it didn't work that way and that I had to plead one way or the other before we could proceed.

I don't know what to do and we hadn't even got started yet. I'm looking back at the guys I'm supposed to be representing, kinda rolling my eyes, lifting my eyebrow up at 'em, trying to get a hint on what to do, sorta like a game show contestant looking to the audience for the right answer on the Price is Right.

"Not guilty, I guess," is my plea and the case is on.

The Feds had a female prosecutor that was ruthless and out for blood, painting up our Family Reunion Dove Shoot and Eat, as some pagan-like slaughter of little birds.

After listening to both sides, (my brilliant defense was that we'd been "planting wheat" this way for years with no trouble), the judge asks the prosecutor if she would negotiate down our fines.

She promptly answered no.

133

When asked why by the judge, she explained that there were more charges they could have written up but didn't, and she wanted us to pay dearly for the infractions that were placed against us.

Then the judge told me that he was going to book this case for a jury trial, (which I perceived to be that he was telling me I could beat this wrap with a jury), but I replied that we wanted to settle this case today and have it done with.

The judge then instructed the prosecutor to go out in the hallway and negotiate our fines down.

A short recess was called and I met in the hall with the prosecutor, my co-defendants gathered up behind me to watch and listen. This turned out to not be a good thing.

I contended we should pay nothing and was quickly rebuked by the prosecutor stating that they had left off game passing charges and over the limit charges against Johnny and his father.

Before I could say a word in defense I was jerked out of the way by Johnny, who inserted himself in the lady prosecutor's face, reading her the riot act on Game Warden conduct, poking her in the chest with his finger and not using any delicate or gentlemanly words so crucial in a borderline case such as this.

The Federal Female Prosecutor was shocked, appalled and stiffened up like a board at Johnny's tirade, bolting for the courtroom door, stating that negotiations were over, full fines would be paid.

Charlie, Ben and Mr. Leston all tackled Johnny, pulling 'em out of the young woman's face, and I caught her at the door, begging her forgiveness for the wild behavior of our friend. (Us knowing how outspoken Johnny is, how he can't hide his feelings or emotions and that he doesn't mince words when he feels he's been wronged, we shouldn't have gotten him near her).

Anyway after I calm her down a little she consents to

lowering our fines to two hundred each and I readily agree, knowing we're lucky to get that after Johnny's explosion.

Lawyering is not as easy it looks.

Mullet Bombs

It was an overcast chilly night, damp and gloomy with no moon.

But there was a big bunch of Run Mullet, mullet with the Red Roe in 'em, holed up in the deep man-made canals at Shell Point.

Johnny, who fished those canals in a row skiff for twenty years, had located 'em and recruited Billy and me to take our mullet skiffs and we'd try to catch us a few thousand pounds of 'em. Using three boats and all the net they can carry we might be able to bust up the school enough to get 'em to hit the net.

Mullet don't like to be caught. They avoid it at all costs, and they are very good at times at not getting caught. That's why these big schooling bunches of fish like to hang-up in the deep canals. They've got lots of places to go for cover, like under the wide-floating docks and they specially like to cram-up under the dozens and dozens of yachts and sailboats. You can put all the net out you want to down the center of the canal and if you can't get the school of fish busted up and separated they'll just stay in a big flowing school moving up or down the canal avoiding the net altogether, you don't catch anything.

That's why Johnny called us in. If we could find the fish all together in one canal, we could use the net on one boat to block the mouth, (these are dead-end canals), and the other two boats could lace all their nets, (probably a combined 1800 yards), in every available piece of open water, trying to get the bunch of fish split-up so they'd get panicked and hit the net.

We came up with an idea that we thought might help us out, just an experiment, something that might help "move" the fish a little bit.

There were a few M-80 firecrackers left over from the Fourth of July. We got some net-leads, some rubber bands and sorta lashed the M-80s to the net leads so they would sink quick.

I loaded 'em in my pocket along with a two-dollar cigar I bought just for the occasion. I had 'em with me when we left the dock at midnight to meet J.R. and Billy at Shell Point.

We got there about thirty minutes late. We were delayed cause we ran thru a nice pod of fish on the way over and had to stop and catch a couple hundred pounds. Only Billy is there waiting on us. He tells me that J.R. has gone on ahead in his paddle skiff to scout the four canals out to see which one the fish are ganged-up in. He goes on to tell me that J.R. had been gone about thirty minutes and he would signal by flicking-his-Bic, his cigarette lighter, at the mouth of the proper canal.

We soon see 'em flicking-his-Bic, telling us to come on.

He's at the mouth of the center canal and he has already got it sealed off from side to side with his deep trammel net.

We're whispering and being real quiet cause the canal banks are lined shoulder to shoulder with private homes and we're not wanting to draw much attention.

Ben and I row down to the end of the canal, throw out the end of the six hundred yards of net we've got and start laying the rest of it out in a zig-zag pattern, working back toward the mouth of the canal.

Billy is using an electric trolling motor rigged up to his mullet skiff to lay his nets out in the center section.

J.R. is lacing the remainder of his net from sea wall to sea wall.

When we're all through striking our nets off it looks like the canal is covered in corks.

There is not any net left on our boat and Ben is slowly pushing us down the center of the canal with the oars.

I'm sitting on the very tip of the bow, my legs

hanging off the front, lighting my cigar, then digging in my coat pocket for a new invention to help the fish move.

The water is slick and all is completely quiet except for the occasional swish of the water as Ben pushes the oar blades thru it.

I'm sticking my cigar to the fuse on that M-80, tossing it overboard as soon as it starts to sputter and spit, sorta pitching it underneath a big sailboat that the fish like to go and hide-out under.

There's a bright burst of light like a flashbulb going off on the bottom of the canal and then a sharp "thrump" of sound, that you can feel vibrate the boat more than you can hear it.

Fish jump out of the water, seemingly timed to the exact instant of the M-80s going off.

Corks start to shake.

Ben's slowly pushing me down the center of the canal with the oars. I'm lighting mullet bombs and pitching 'em left and right, making the mullet move from their dark safe hidey-holes around the big keels of those sailboats.

Billy and George have drifted up against the seawall and are doubled-up laughing, both of 'em about to choke to death cause they're trying to be quiet to not draw attention.

I pitch my last mullet-bomb under their boat just to liven things up a little and they can't hold it back and laughter is the only sound other than fish jumping and rattling the corkline.

All three boats begin taking up net, shucking fish into the box, the success of the catch marked by the constant thump thump sound of fish being tossed into the iceboxes and that's an almost continual sound cause the mullet bombs moved the fish pretty well, making 'em eat that monofilament up.

We came out of that canal with three to five hundred pounds per boat which wasn't great but it wasn't bad.

The pity of the situation was that I had used up all the mullet bombs, not saving any for our next set in the back canal. As it turned out, we didn't need any fish movers on that set of the nets. Unknown to us that back canal was so full of fish that we couldn't have hauled all the fish out, if we had caught anymore than we did.

We repeated the same attack plan in the back canal that we used in the middle canal. Johnny sealed the end off the Billy and I deployed our nets in the center and in the end section of that body of water.

All was quiet.

Not a fish jumping or swirling.

It's about five-thirty a.m. and it's sorta foggy and misty with just the hint of a brightening in the east from the new day coming.

It's time to take up our nets, clear out of this area before the residents wake up and start trying to take their sailboats and yachts out, which at the present time would be impossible cause of the eighteen hundred yards of gill-net that's laced and crossed thru every stretch of available water.

I row the boat over to the end of our net so we can begin tripping it on the net table, not expecting much of a catch cause there is only a few corks shaking indicating fish gilled-off.

Ben reaches down and drags the end of the net onto the table and boy are we surprised.

There's no fish hardly at all in the upper six foot part of the net, but the last two feet of webbing next to the lead-line looks like there's a fish in every mesh.

We're not even going to try to clear the mullet out of the net as we bring it in, we're just going to rope net, fish and all on the boat, get out of this canal into the open bay before daylite.

Billy and George in their mullet skiff are doing the same thing, they're going to have a load and when Ben and I row up to where Johnny is, with his deep trammel net, I can see that he's up to his waist in net and fish.

That morning is etched in my memory forever.

The sky getting pink, the mist rising off the black slick water. The sound of oars pushing hard to move the boats that are sitting low, rails barely above the water from the loads of mullet roped in and distributed evenly, so the boats won't sink.

Between the three boats we had close to six thousand pounds, Johnny out-catching Billy and I with that deep trammel net, he had about twenty-five hundred by himself.

I'm glad I was out of mullet bombs cause if I'd had any left we would probably have sunk ourselves trying to get those fish out.

Kittens

I opened the door to go out and get the newspaper. It was early morning, before daylite. I was in kind of a hurry because I had to meet a Japanese college professor, a jelly-fish expert, for breakfast at the Waffle House.

Anyway when I opened the door there were these scrawny, ugly, tiny kittens meowing and crying around the doorstep.

I'm calling for my wife, Mary Jane, and I'm not happy. It's early, I'm still tired from the day before and here's another variable thrown in.

M.J.'s picking up the little kitties, petting 'em, hugging 'em, getting food for 'em.

I've got to go meet the Jelly-Fish Man.

All that day we're dragging nets for jelly-fish, learning how to clean 'em, how to process the jelly-fish into food, all supervised by the Jelly-Fish Man. A long exhausting day.

I always try to check in with my wife around six in the evening and when I call her on this particular day I ask about the kittens that had shown up that morning.

She tells me the little cats are fine and that two more have shown up, all from the same litter.

"Great," I think, a whole house full of kittens, soon to be CATS and I already have four or five dozen terrorizing my seafood restaurant and fish-house.

Over the next few weeks Mary Jane nurses the kitties into good health and manages to only give one away to her sister. (These are real ugly kittens, everybody knows they're going to be extra-ugly cats when they're grown)

Anyway, the half-grown kittens can't be given away and they have to go.

I volunteer to take all the weaned kittens to Spring Creek to join in the ranks of fish-house and restaurant cats colonized there.

After a week or two of constant persuasion Mary Jane finally agrees.

I've got a small animal cage that's been around the restaurant for years and I bring it home to transport the kitties to Spring Creek.

Early the next morning I catch-up all the little kittens and put 'em in the cage in the back of my truck. I run back in the house and refill my coffee cup to drive the thirty miles to work.

Mary Jane's petting and saying bye-bye to the little kitties, sorry to see 'em go, still trying to convince me that we should keep the ugliest one, one she has named Nosey cause of a lite-yellow stripe that runs down the cat's nose.

I'm telling her that all the little kittens are going to be fine, I'll take good care of 'em and she can visit with 'em when she comes to Spring Creek.

I kiss her good-bye, jump in my truck and out the driveway we go, glad to be getting these soon-to-be-cats off of my land and my sincere intentions are to turn 'em loose at Spring Creek to make their best with the rest of the pack.

Tallahassee traffic on U.S. 90 and Capital Circle between 7 a.m. and 9 a.m. is terrible.

Stop and Go.

Bumper to bumper for miles.

Two-lane to four-lanes to six-lanes back to two-lanes. Packed, jammed, dangerous, awful traffic.

I finally reach the What-a-Burger on Appalachee Parkway where I stop and get my Breakfast-on-a-Bun and my sweet tea every morning. A tradition in my life at that time.

While I'm waiting at the drive-thru window for my order to get ready I decide to get out of my truck and check on the kittens in the cage.

I glance in the cage and I'm stunned.

I stare in disbelief.

Then I become baffled and confused.

There are no little kitties in the cage.

Not one.

They are gone and I'm trying to remember if I really put five kittens in there, but I know I did.

Then I become horrified, picturing those little kittens squeezing out of that cage and jumping out of the back of the truck into all that thick, aggressive, jammed-up traffic I'd just driven thru on Capital Circle, and those poor little kittens being mashed and squashed and run-over by all the thousands of cars behind me.

God, the thought is awful but I must never let Mary Jane know.

I can't even eat my Breakfast-on-a-toasted-hamburger-bun, with mayo, cheese, bacon and eggs.

I can barely sip my sweet tea.

I fret over it til I get to Spring Creek, hop in my mullet boat and go chase fish for the day, forgetting the squashed kitties for a while.

At the end of my fishing-day I start my restaurant-working-night, and like I mentioned before I like to call home around 6 or 6:30 to check in.

I call the house and Mary Jane answers. We talk about the kids, what we've each been doing during the day, our usual evening conversation.

Finally she asks the question I knew was coming.

"How are the kittens?" she asks.

"Oh, they're fine," I say, with awful thoughts of those poor kitties jumping out of the truck, playing thru my head.

There's about a five-second pause and then:

"LIAR," shouts Mary Jane, "LIAR," she yells again.

I'm speechless, dumbstruck, shocked cause she's never spoken to me like that before, she musta seen 'em flattened on the highway, I'm thinking.

I'm silent on the phone.

Then Mary Jane starts laughing, high pitched pealing

laughter, laughing so hard she can hardly talk. Telling me how silly I looked driving down the driveway, sipping on my coffee and all those kittens jumping outta the back of my truck like popcorn, and all those little kitties being back in her arms and around her feet before I'd even left the yard.

And here I'd been living in misery all day long thinking about those poor little kitties, the kitties that M.J. cared so much for being mashed flat on Capital Circle and all the time they had been safe and sound at home with their momma.

We ended up keeping the ugliest one, Nosey.

Two more we finally gave away.

And two kittens, finally made the full trip to Spring Creek where their offspring mark their unique ugliness to this day.

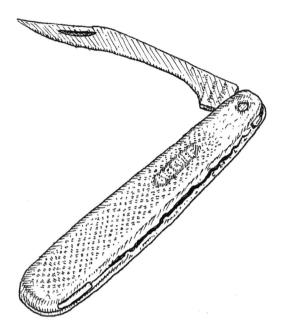

Old Pocket Knife

Ms. Barbara give me this knife sometime in the mid 1980's. It was sort of a Christmas present that she handed out to all of the gill-net fishermen that had been bringing in swinging boat loads of mullet that fall.

I immediately liked it.

It was a single-blade folding knife, with a thin, stainless steel blade that was four and a half inches long. The handle was aluminum and flat, light weight, and it fit perfect in the back, left-hand pocket of a pair of jeans.

I've almost worn it out. Sharpening it so many times

the blade is a needle shaped dagger, whetstoned down into the thick top-part of the knife, but still razor sharp.

The handle of the knife, that's cast aluminum, is cracked the full length of its spine from being opened and closed so much, and from beating on carburetors and battery connections trying to get some engine to start.

I've lost this pocket knife three or four times from it wearing a hole in my back pocket and escaping without me even knowing he was gone.

But it always showed back up, even though one time it was gone for six months, suddenly appearing in the hand of one of our commercial fishermen that was cleaning mullet beside me at the fishhouse. He was happy to give it back when he saw how glad I was to see it.

The more I think about and look at this wore-out old knife the more things come to mind that it's cut on———

Skinning Clay's first buck in Georgia.

Clipping hundreds of doves' feet off their legs before you fry 'em, quail too.

Scaling buckets full of bream and bass.

Ripping the guts out of thousands and thousands of pounds of Amberjack and Grouper, some of the jacks going over a hundred pounds.

Skinning squirrels and rabbits.

Cracking Stone Crab claws and pecans.

Butchering hogs.

Filleting boatloads of mullet, splitting out roe.

Skinning catfish and blowfish.

Minor surgery on myself and others removing fish hooks, splinters, and fish fins from heads, hands, arms and legs.

Cutting hooks from pelicans.

Opening oysters and scallops.

Slicing tomatoes, squash, cucumbers and any other vegetable grown in the South, lotsa cabbage and tons of onion to fry with anything else you were frying.

I've drawn it out of my pocket and used it to cut tough

steaks that have been served to me in restaurants.

Smeared gallons of mayonnaise and mustard on bread for sandwiches.

I've cut myself with it numerous times, sometimes pretty bad now that I think about it, this knife has drawn plenty of my blood.

It has saved me more than once.

Deftly slicing a net in two, just in time to keep the boat from sinking when the current had fouled our net around a channel marker in the St. Marks River, trying to drag us under.

I've rigged crab traps with it.

Used it hanging in gill nets and seines.

Cut up crab bait.

Sliced thousands of limes.

Rigged multiple-hook grouper and amberjack lines.

Used it in net-hanging, wire skinning, as a hammer and a pry bar.

I've used it more than once to cut bouquets of wildflowers for my wife.

This old pocket knife has ridden quietly and reliably in my back pocket on most all the adventures I've been on the last twenty years.

I find it amazing that it hasn't been lost overboard in all that time.

It is still not too late.

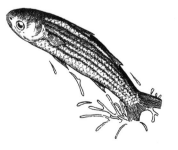

Fuel

I think I've figured it out.

I have finally, through much pondering, have got the answer to heart attacks, stroke, cancer, all the big ones.

It's the amount of fuel we've got.

I think we're all given the same amount of life-time fuel and we can each individually burn it up at our own discretion.

Fast or slow.

A slow start at the beginning of our lives, conserving fuel and then wide-open at the end, or wide-open from the start to end, or moderate speed of life, stretching it out for a long time.

But when the allotted amount of life-time fuel is burnt-up the motor stops.

Conserve it when you can.

Save it for when you need to put lots of your allocation of fuel to the situation and try to conserve and enjoy the time when you don't need to be burning much and don't think that physical activity necessarily burns the most fuel, cause I think you probably burn more fuel in your head with worry and stress.

But when the fuel's gone the whole system breaks down and the heart attack, the cancer, the stroke or whatever jumps in and shuts us down, telling the world that it's time for someone new to see what they can do and how far they can go on their full tank.

A Bad Week

Trandice Spellwright worked part-time as a waitress for us.

She was trying to change her life. She had worked for twenty-years as a commercial fisherwoman, gill-netting off Louisiana, dragging seines with her daddy and brothers, she even worked for a while on shrimp boats that stayed offshore for thirty days at the time. Trandice once told me that by the twentieth day out, on the thirty day trip, that she would of whipped every man's ass on the boat.

Her being the only girl on board you can probably guess why.

Trandice is a big girl, well over two hundred pounds, strong as an ox, witty and not one bit shy. She's brazen to a point of being almost rude but she smiles and laughs and that helps make up for some of the things she says, and she'll say most anything that comes in her mind.

I like her, enjoy working with her, she keeps things lively to say the least.

She comes from a long line of commercial fisherman and a big big family, twelve or thirteen kids. Most all the Spellwrights work in some fishery or the other, a pretty wild, tough, big bunch they are. You can see where Trandice gets her personality and her big strong body by knowing her family.

Like I said she was trying to change her life. Nearing forty years of age she was being worn down by fishing and shrimping and was trying to make a go of it on the hill, (land), by waiting tables. She worked two jobs, one was at Rosey's Restaurant full-time and then she worked a couple of nights a week for us at Spring Creek.

At Rosey's Restaurant all the wait people pool and split their tips after the lunch shift. This is a pretty good system unless you've got a thief in the group that pockets some of the tips instead of pooling 'em all in the tip bucket.

There was a waiter at Rosey's that was related to the family that owned the restaurant, and was bad about stuffing money in his pocket and still wanting his full share at split-up time.

Trandice complained over and over to the management about the unfair practice but they never did anything about it.

Trandice finally resorted to threats of physical violence, telling waiter-boy she was going to stomp his ass if he didn't quit stealing.

That didn't work. He kept right on stealing, getting sorta cocky about it, ignoring Trandice's threats.

One winter day Trandice came into Rosey's to wait tables and she wasn't feeling too good. She was real upset about a health problem she was having with her most beloved sausage-dog. You could tell that she had been crying. On top of that she had a real bad cold which made her extra miserable and ill-tempered.

On that day, toward the end of the shift, waiter-boy steals one tip too many and Trandice sees 'em do it.

Not a word she says about it.

When the shift is over the tips are split up and all the wait-people head out to their cars in the parking lot.

Trandice is right behind Waiter-boy, following 'em.

I have an eyewitness account to the following event.

Waiter-boy senses Trandice is behind 'em as he reaches his car. One quick look at her scowling face tells 'em he's in danger. He snatches his car door open trying to dive in for safety, but Trandice catches 'em by his arm and drags 'em out saying, "I told you what would happen if you kept stealing my money."

Waiter-boy breaks loose and starts to run, yelling for his Aunt at the top of his lungs.

Trandice easily catches 'em by the back of his collar and drags Waiter-boy back to her as easily as lifting a small bream out of a pond on a big cane pole.

Now we must address Trandice's clothing for a minute.

She always dresses neat, wearing a white satiny shirt with big ruffles around the collar and down the front. She also wears the shortest denim mini-skirt you've ever seen to cover her ample bottom. The skirt length is a good foot above the knee, showing plenty of her strong, thick, stocking wrapped thighs.

As Waiter-boy screams, feet running like the wind but not going anywhere, Trandice starts telling 'em in fisherman's terms about his thievin' ways and she's kicking 'em in the ass as hard and fast as she can, while she's holding 'em by the collar. Every kick makes that mini-skirt ride higher and higher. By the third kick the skirt is up over Trandice's waist showing all her kicking-gear and she's starting to cry.

Waiter-boy is spinning his wheels and shrieking for his Aunt.

Trandice is cussin', crying' and kickin'.

After eight or ten good kicks, Trandice with a big sob, spins Waiter-boy around and lays 'em out in the parking lot with a round-house right. She leaves her skirt up around her waist and marches to her truck, still crying and drives away.

The tip stealing stopped.

Now back to the sausage-dog I mentioned before.

Trandice's best friend in the world was her little dog. She loved 'em.

Somehow her little dog got out of the house and wandered next door and got himself caught by a real mean bulldog. The bulldog had gotten little sausage-dog by the throat and shook 'em a few times, as is their nature. The neighbors heard the little dog squealing and broke up the murder before it could happen.

Little sausage-dog was lucky but he had received a sort of unusual wound. A small hole had been torn in the skin of his throat. Every time he would get excited and start barking, air somehow, would get sucked in between his skin and his body and blow 'em up like a balloon. The more he'd bark the bigger he would get, even swelling out his little pencil-thin tail to the size of a fat sausage.

Trandice would get horrified seeing her little pet get all blowed-up like a blow-fish, legs not able to reach the ground till he'd just roll over on his side, like a football-with-paws sticking out, still trying to bark but mostly just squeaking and swelling up even more.

She would start crying and rush 'em to the vet's office. The vet would lay the bloated pooch on a table and start at his fat tail and squeeze and mash like you do a toothpaste tube, pushing the air back out the hole in the throat, the escaping air sounding just like a balloon does when you blow it up and then hold the intake hole and spread it tight to make that squeally noise.

When all the air was out the vet would tape up the hole.

Somehow the tape came off and poor ole Trandice had to take the dog back to have the air worked out of 'em again.

Trandice works for us on Saturday nights and we were closing down the restaurant. I was closing out the cash register and Trandice was sweeping the floor, looking kind of depressed, shuffling along, sweeping slow, gloomy acting.

Totally unlike herself, specially at closing time, usually she's full-of-it.

I notice Trandice's somber mood and yell out to her across the room, "Hey Gal, what's wrong with you, you look kinda down."

She stops sweeping, leans on her broom and she says as serious as can be; "Leo, I've had a bad week." "I've had a deathly cold, I had to beat up a queer, and I've had to deflate my dog twice."

Buck on the Shell Point Cutoff

It was in November, cool but not cold.

I had shut down the restaurant and had gone to the Junior Store for gas for my skiff.

I wasn't in any hurry cause I had an hour to kill, waiting for the tide to go mullet fishing.

Instead of coming straight back down the Spring Creek Highway, I decided to ride down the Shell Point Road and cut over to Spring Creek down the cut-off road.

The cut-off road is a canopy dirt road that's bordered on each side by a classic Florida swamp.

It's a pretty road day or night and there's plenty of wildlife to see from reptiles to deer.

I had just turned off the Shell Point Road, going slow cause this dirt road is kinda wash-board when the weather's dry.

I saw a set of eyes glowing at me not a hundred yards down the road.

Deer eyes.

I kept motoring along slow till the whole deer lit up in my headlights.

What a deer. A real nice eight-point, standing tall and proud facing me straight-on.

I stopped the truck about fifty yards from the buck, us just facing each other, looking.

I'm feeling behind the seat for my old 870 twelve-gauge, grasping it by the barrel and pulling it up into my hands.

I jack a double-ought buckshot into the barrel still staring at those big horns.

The deer wheels around and starts trotting away.

As I'm thinking that the chance is lost to shoot 'em, the buck wheels around and starts trotting straight toward the truck.

The deer takes a few prancing steps and stops, trying to look through the headlights, ears up, neck stretched, tall and proud.

He prances toward the truck some more, thirty yards away, stops and looks hard at the truck again.

I've forgot all about shooting 'em, curious at the deer's actions.

He keeps on coming straight for the dead-center of the pick-up, like a head-on collision, except he stops five feet in front of the hood.

That deer is looking so hard through the truck, trying to look around the truck, intent on something besides the truck and then I realize that a doe must have passed close behind me and that's where his attention lay.

The nice eight-point walks to within two feet of my front bumper, headlights on, motor running. The deer makes a right turn, at a slow walk, like you would do to walk around a car in a parking lot.

The crazy buck makes the turn at the front fender and starts walking slow down the side of my truck, having to make a short detour around my driver's-side mirror to keep from bumping into it.

My window's down, my gun's in my lap and I'm looking this trophy-size buck in the eye as he pauses by the driver's door, so close I could have slapped 'em in the face.

That deer is so intent on whatever is behind me, (his lady friend?), that he doesn't even know I'm there or the danger he could be in.

I don't know why I didn't reach out and touch 'em, I didn't even think about shooting 'em, I was too amazed at watching 'em and how stupid or addled he seemed to be.

When the boy-deer gets the girl-deer on their minds they just ain't got no sense, no caution, and act just plain stupid sometimes.

I reckon deer are a lot like people in some things.

Knots

There are lots of books about knots. Famous knots, knots with all kinds of names for all kinds of purposes. Clove hitches, timber hitches, square knots, bosun's hitch, fisherman's knot, half-hitches, etc., etc. and on and on and on.

I like the Granny knot myself.

It's basic and simple. Everybody learns it when they start tying their own shoes.

Twist the rope or line around itself and pull it tight, twist the line around itself and pull it tight again.

It will hold in most cases.

And it will get real real tight if you put some pressure on it.

Have a good sharp knife ready to cut it loose cause you won't untie it.

It's a good knot to use in the dark and you're trying to get an anchor line tied to the boat in rough seas and you're perched on the bow-cap trying to keep from being thrown overboard.

It's a no-brainer type knot that's good in emergencies or when you're scared.

I've caught big fish, hundred pounders, using the Granny.

I've secured big boats in heavy seas with it.

Tied my shoes with it.

Pulled trucks out of bog holes with it.

A simple knot.

Sometimes the best knots come loose.

Daemeon Dimes

Daemeon Dimes is the son of, the grandson of, the great-grandson of true commercial fishermen. He was brought up oystering, shrimping and gill-net fishing for mullet.

He was good at it.

Specially the gill-netting part of it.

He was born to it, raised in it, prospered from it, steeped in the thrill, the chase, the challenge, the excitement and the money of it.

Gill-net fishing was really all he knew or cared about and was all he wanted to do even though the State outlawed it in 1995. Daemeon could take his mullet skiff and a few hundred yards of monofilament gill net and keep his bills paid-up and money in his pocket.

The Dimes family were some of the best and longest lasting gill-net fishermen on the Gulf of Mexico. Catching fish and surviving, (not prosperous anymore), despite the net ban.

But it was tough.

Enough background, on to the story.

Daemeon ran a mullet skiff that was about three feet longer and one foot wider than "My Ole Mullet Skiff" pictured earlier in the book. I ran a 40 horsepower motor on my boat and had all the power I needed.

Daemeon had a souped-up mullet skiff. He had somehow managed to bolt a two hundred and twenty five horsepower Yamaha outboard motor in the tunnel on his boat and what he had was a water-bound rocket. Water-bound some of the time but most times only the foot of the motor was in the water, the bottom of the boat just barely skimming the wave tops, the thrust and power of that 225 lifting the boat out of the water.

It was fast.

It needed to be fast to buy time, time needed to untie

nets, dump nets or just get away clean cause the FMP couldn't catch up with 'em or follow 'em through the complicated series of oyster bars in the bay.

But after dozens of get-aways and close calls the odds run against you sometimes.

This was one of those times.

It's midnight during mullet-roe season. Daemeon's loaded down with six-hundred yards of illegal, outlawed, violation of the Constitution of the State of Florida, monofilament gill-net. He's behind on his payments, broke, hunting a load of fish. He's idling along with no lights on in front of Bottoms seine-yard, one of the only hard-sand stretches of shoreline with drive-to access on our marshy coastline.

Unfortunately an under-cover, night-visioned pair of Florida Marine Patrol officers are laying on watch in the marsh grass.

Before Daemeon even knows they are there the FMP sneaks up to his boat and grabs hold of it, yelling at 'em to freeze.

He's caught.

Red-handed with the horrible gill-net neatly stacked on the stern ready to strike off.

A violation of the Constitution to possess that net and that net being his family's only tool to make a living with.

Anyway the FMP's got 'em. They are calling in back-up to meet 'em at the seine yard.

All the night duty patrollers and especially the high-ranking officers, like Lt. Robby Barfus, want to be in on the excitement and arrest one of the infamous Dimes boys.

The mighty high-dollar techno hunters have bagged their game.

Poor Daemeon.

The FMP beaches Daemeon's boat side-ways to the shoreline, it pointing up and down the beach instead of straight into it.

The FMP boat is beached back behind it.

The troops arrive, blue-lights flashing on their trucks, jeeps and boats, radios blaring, walkie-talkies screeching. They all gather around Daemeon's boat, flashing spotlights up and down his rig, inspecting his nets and deem them "a major violation".

A conference is called by Commanding Officer Lt. Robby Barfus and all the troops gather around the hood of one of the FMP trucks. The Grand Lt. is pointing and giving orders while the troopers hold their flash lites high over their heads, lighting up the maps and the trucks and Lt. Robby Barfus like props and players on a stage.

All this time Daemeon is just sitting in the chair on the driving platform, built high above that powerful motor, looking dejected, sad-and-mad all at the same time, not saying much.

The boat is gently rocking in the light chop long-ways against the shore.

That 225 Yamaha is still down in the tunnel, not tilted-up as it usually would be cause there's a deep drop off at the seine yard beach on low tide.

The nite is dark.

The orders from the Lieutenant are given to the troops.

Two troopers are ordered to follow Daemeon's boat closely and one trooper is ordered to accompany Daemeon, and Daemeon is instructed , in no uncertain terms, to proceed directly to the launch-ramp at Fiddlers Point, about a half-mile away, and load his boat on the trailer. There he will be formally charged.

Daemeon nods his head in acknowledgement. He's still sitting at the steering wheel, in the Captain's seat, at the starter switch and the throttle of his rocket.

The FMP officer to "accompany" Daemeon wades out and shoves the mullet skiff off the shoreline.

Lt. Robby Barfus yells down further instructions to

the "accompanying" FMP man and distracts 'em for two seconds and that's long enough.

Daemeon cranks that willing Yamaha, and in a shove-of-the-throttle, blasts his rocket off into the night-black bay, headed for the launch ramp as per his instructions, in a wide-open, round about manner.

The supposed-to-accompany FMP man and the supposed-to, "follow closely" FMP boat and officers are still standing on the hill, mouths open, dumbstruck.

Daemeon's boat is completely out of sight and almost out of hearing before the covey of FMP birds can burst into flight.

The "to follow closely" boat is told to pursue and chase.

The four FMP vehicles scramble, spinning tires, turning on their blue-lites, their sirens, two of 'em taking off to the north on Bottoms Road to race their way to known boat ramps and two vehicles turn left to drag-race to the ramp at Fiddlers Point to try to see or hear Daemeon's boat go by.

An all-points-bulletin is issued and I think the National Guard may have been put on alert.

The two FMP trucks dispatched to the Fiddlers Point boat ramp slam on brakes and slide into the parking lot, blue-lites flashing. The headlights on their vehicles light up the scene at the ramp.

There is Daemeon's truck and trailer, backed down to the water in preparation to load up his boat.

And there is Daemeon and his boat, he has it hooked to the winch on the trailer, has tilted up his giant motor and is cranking the whole rig up on his boat trailer as he was instructed to do.

But the net is gone.

The evidence is gone.

The one and only thing that a "major violation case" could be made on is no longer in existence.

Daemeon is smiling now, cranking the winch,

putting his boat on the trailer to go home.

"What net?" he's saying, "We ain't got no illegal net and no fish either." "What we done wrong?" he asks, looking happy, ready to talk.

The FMP troopers march off for another truck-hood flashlite illuminated, animated confused conference.

Lt. Robby Barfus walks back to Daemeon fuming and says: "You got us that time boy, you surely did, yeah, real slick."

Lt. Barfus hands Daemeon a minor ticket for improper life vests, the only violation they could hang on 'em, a thirty-five dollar ticket.

He tells Daemeon again, "Yeah, you got us that time but it won't happen again," then he adds, "Your time's coming and we'll get you yet."

And the FMP loaded up and drove away.

And they got Daemeon later.

But he made 'em work for it.

The FMP ran 'em day and night with planes, helicopters, airboats, undercover boats, launch ramp surveillance, night vision scopes, souped-up power boats and jet-skis.

He quit fishing for a while from the stress and frayed nerves. Just the strain from the pressure made 'em try regular work, like laying fiber-optic cable, but the money they paid wouldn't pay the bills.

He went back to gill-net fishing out of pure necessity.

He needed money for electricity, food and payments and his Grandma's fish market was completely out of mullet which they needed to survive.

The mullet in the bay and the retail market on the hi-way supported everybody in the family and had done so for generations.

Daemeon had to go cause that's all he knows, everybody's bills can get paid from a good trip in the bay.

But the odds have caught up again.

Daemeon is at the right place at the wrong time or

the wrong place at the right time or something.

That night the FMP is hiding in a duck blind on the grass flats off Piney Island when Daemeon cruises by late at night.

The law throws a spot light on his boat and yells for him to stop.

Daemeon cuts the afterburners in on that big Yamaha blowing out of sight before the FMP can back their boat out of the duck blind. He runs at full speed about a mile out to the reef where he dumps his gill net, at a place he can return to later.

He's not even going to try and fish tonite.

He has decided that he's going home, early and empty handed.

No fish, no money, no nothin'.

Daemeon's running his rocketized mullet skiff in a long, leisurely curving run toward the Panacea Channel to load-up and go home.

No net, no fish on board, no confrontations coming.

Half-way back to the boat landing, where his truck and trailer are parked, an FMP boat starts running 'em down, blue-lights flashing like Hi-way-Patrol-on-the-water.

Daemeon backs off the throttle and stops, knowing he can out-run and out-maneuver the mullet police, but he doesn't need to. He's got everything in order.

The FMP boat pulls alongside with blue-lights flashing, spot lights being blazed into Daemeon and his deck hand's eyes. The officers are yelling for everybody to "freeze" as they're securing one boat to the other.

An officer of the FMP jumps aboard the mullet boat, grabs Daemeon by the coat and drags 'em down from the driving platform.

And twists his hands behind his back.

Puts handcuffs on 'em.

Puts handcuffs on the deck hand too and tells 'em they're under arrest.

They're under arrest for resisting arrest.

And they were taken to jail for it.

No charges to be arrested for like gill-netting or fishing closed seasons, they had no net and they had no fish.

They were just arrested for resisting arrest.

Arrest for what?

How can you be arrested for resisting arrest when you've done nothing to be arrested for in the first place.

The commercial fishing laws in Florida are enforced differently than the rest of the laws that the U.S.A. abides by.

Each officer enforces the law as he personally feels like that day. It's guilty until proven innocent and it costs the individual that's charged a fortune in fines and legal fees to try to keep his rights to make a living.

The mighty FMP "got Daemeon" like they promised.

The traditional inshore fishery in Florida is over.

But I can tell you this:

A bunch of us went down hard trying to keep it going. We were proud then and we're still proud now.

Slowing Down

The wind was blowing, our first Northwester and it was late in the year. I knew the mullet should be bunchin' up cause it was way past time for the first run of fish.

I'm thinking of where I need to run that mullet boat to, and what kind of tide I'll have to get there on.

It's 10 p.m. after the restaurant is closed.

I've only put in about 14 hours and I'm fixing to put 10 more in to try and make a full day.

Put on a good warm jacket.

An extra pair of socks, wool over cotton.

A tee shirt, a long sleeve shirt, a sweatshirt - then the jacket.

You're starting to sweat when you put on your slicker pants.

So you know you're dressed just right when you get into that mullet skiff, full of gas, hundred and fifty pounds of ice, battery for the take-up lite, six hundred yards of net and hit the bay.

Excited, challenged, charged, on guard, Ready.

Looking for the fish, running thru the bay, feeling the cold wind in your face; anticipating the catch.

Marveling at the stars, watching the black water, feeling absolutely free to turn yourself loose in the great wide-open to make-it-if-you-can.

Can't wait to close the restaurant down, get geared up and go, but tonite I can wait.

It's been ten years or so, or a lifetime ago that I've been that fired-up.

Twenty, twenty-five years of days-on-end expended energy has caught-up.

The Net-Ban and the rules and regulations have added more than half the burden.

I'm just listening to the wind now, thinking where I ought to be, mentally icing the boat, gassing it up, checking the gear.

I'm just sitting on the porch, thinking about it, wishing for it, wondering if I would still have the energy to go.

Excitement creates energy and I'm just not as excited about it as I used to be.

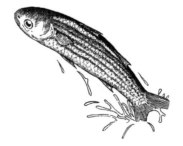

TURKEY

/CLAY MARSHALL LOVEL 2-5-02

First Turkey

Old Ned owned a piece of land off of Meridian Road that was long and narrow, maybe eighty acres. It was bordered on all three sides by the Phelps Plantation and everybody knew that place held all the deer and turkeys in the world.

Old Ned didn't mind one bit in the world if we came in his driveway and parked in the woods behind his house, hiding our cars so we could slip around the edge of the Phelps place. We were always dropping by some venison or squirrels or coots or ducks we'd shot, sometimes a coon or live possum we'd caught. Ned sorta liked the situation, he was gettin' too old to hunt anymore.

I had just gotten my driver's license, was able to expand my huntin' territory, so after school one Friday afternoon I went out to Ned's. I was just slipping around the fence line with my .22 rifle, scouting mostly, when a big flock of turkeys started flowing out into the wide clean-plowed firebreak that was cut along the perimeter of all the Phelps land.

I had never shot a turkey before and want to real bad.

There's three grown gobblers, half a dozen jakes and a bunch of hens pecking at everything on the ground and running after everything that hopped, darted or flew and catching most of 'em.

I'm standing up behind a big oak that's on the edge of the firebreak, peering around the tree at that busy mass of turkeys doing their thing.

One gobbler is strutting.

The jakes are running at each other, chasing each other around and mock-fighting, preparing themselves for when their spurs are sharp and they are old enough to fight for the hens.

The hens are not concerned with much of anything, paying no attention to the strutting or the fighting. They are non-stop movement, continually walking and pecking around, scratching at the ground, food is their main event.

The birds are over a hundred yards away, too far to shoot and I'm excited as can be, wanting to aim and fire so bad, but I know it would be a waste.

The sun is going down, it's getting late and all the turkeys drizzle off into the woods and never come close enough to get shot at.

As soon as the last one disappears I slip off back to my car planning to come back early the next morning with a bigger gun, something that will reach out further and bag me a turkey.

I'm all excited relating my turkey story to Hurley, my high-school buddy, a teammate on the high-school football team, partner in refining our poaching techniques. We double dated together, drank our first hard liquor together, killed and caught piles of game and fish together.

And he was certainly going to accompany me on our first turkey ambush cause he had never killed a turkey either and his Daddy owned a gun I needed to borrow.

We chose our weapons with care.

We chose the only two rifles that Hurley's Daddy would let us use.

Hurley got a .222 bolt action with a scope. I got a .223 pump with iron sights and no clip to find anywhere, meaning I'd have to load one shell in the barrel and only get one shot.

We had the right gear.

We're going to the right place.

And we did.

Before daylight I'm crouched behind that same oak I'd watched the birds from the evening before.

It's just breaking a fall daylight, real cool almost cold, just before a frost. The sky was slightly overcast and there was a thin cloudy mist drifting a few feet off the ground, flowing uphill like a ghostly river, weightless and suspended, disappearing completely as it rises through the tree tops and crosses the firebreak that is sloping downhill like a dirt river toward the east.

Hurley's five feet above me, perched on a big limb, leaning against the trunk. The darkness is getting weaker and the sun lite getting stronger. We're intent looking down the firebreak that's bordered on one side by virgin long-leaf pine woods rolling down to a hardwood bottom. On the other side of the clean strip a fence, that marks Old Ned's property that was thick with regrowth gum, oak and hickory.

Two birds step out a hundred and fifty yards away and start to work their way uphill toward us. One bird is always alert, looking around as the other one scratches, pecks and feeds, both of 'em always moving, walking at a leisurely pace but synchronized in the sense that as soon as the pecking-feeding turkey raises up and goes on guard, the bird that had been on watch starts pecking around.

But they're coming on.

Getting closer.

Steady walking, eating and watching.

"I'll take the one on the right," I say as I'm hugging that single shot rifle up tight, that I've never fired before, filling those iron vee-shaped sights full of turkey, the bead on the end of the barrel a light colored speck, wavering around the body of that bird, and Hurley says, "I'll take the one on the left and we'll shoot on the count of three."

"O.K." I whisper back, tightening down on that .223 and Hurley whispers, "One".

I'm focused down the barrel of that Remington, listening for the quarter-back to call the count.

"Two," I hear murmured from above me, my finger taking up slack on the trigger.

The number "Three" was never spoken by word as far as I know, but the .222 residing on the oak limb above me spoke loud and sharp, and the turkey on the left went to flopping around wildly. The turkey on the right stood tall and alert. I finally managed to get my sights lined back up on 'em after being startled by the surprise shot immediately following the exhale of the word "Two", and pulled the trigger.

My bird went to flopping around like crazy too, me up and charging down the damp, fresh-plowed ground, sinking ankle deep every step, wanting to get ahold of that bird.

With a wildman yell Hurley jumps down the limb of the oak into the soft dirt of the lane, ploughing it up as he's chasing his thrashing bird down, both of us catching our turkeys about the same time, laughing and happy, excited, wringing turkey necks with one hand, holding rifles with the other, spreading feathers and making five inch deep tracks like a herd of buffalo, leaving sign that a blindman could see in the dark.

We were happy with our birds, proud, showing 'em off to our family and friends.

And we wanted to shoot another one.

And we went to shoot another one but Hurley couldn't go so his younger, bigger, little-brother Will went, all of us playing high school football together at the time. Will was just a year younger than us but twice as big and strong as we were, a good partner on any huntin' or fishin' expedition and a tough football player on both sides of the line.

Will and I set-up the same way at the same place two mornings later. We just knew that some more of those birds were going to come out where we could get a shot at 'em.

But they don't.

And waiting for an hour or so after good daylight we become bored.

Will whispers down that he can see the bright green of a food plot planted in a hardwood bottom that's just a couple of hundred yards further over on the Phelps place.

We decide to slip our way over to it and see if we can catch a deer feeding in it. We'd be happy to drag some venison home in place of the turkeys.

We ease across the firebreak into the long leaf woods, us sorta staying stooped over cause the brush is low, this being good quail hunting territory. When we got about twenty yards farther onto the Phelps property, two men

175

step out from behind a huge pine tree, glaring at us, waiting for us, one of 'em growling at us to "hold it right there."

Me and Will stop dead in our tracks, both of us frozen in mid-step, big-eyed, mouths open, surprised like two deer in the headlights.

But only for a split second cause by some silent command we both do exactly the opposite of "hold it right there," we "turn it loose to somewhere else," running like scared rabbits through the brush, crossing back over the firebreak and diving head first across the fence to roll, get up, and run some more only to stop and hide in a thicket when we hear the would-be apprehenders cussing at us from the fence cause they were too heavy or too lazy to climb over.

We made out way quickly back to our car, drove out Ned's driveway and I haven't been out to Ned's since, and this all happened in 1967.

176

You Can Not Kill a Bulldog with a Hammer

I didn't do this, but I stood there and witnessed it personally.

We were putting an addition on the kitchen at the restaurant and had hired a contractor to build it.

We'll name him John, and John had a Dalmatian puppy that went everywhere with 'em.

That puppy would play around the job site and most days he had a playmate, the neighbor's pit-bull dog Sam, and Sam was a friendly bulldog, all-white, medium build. Most the time wagging his stump of a tail, frolicking with John's Dalmatian, enjoying the company.

Bruce and I are scaling and filleting mullet behind the restaurant.

John's setting trusses wearing his tool belt, 20 oz. Estwing claw-hammer in hand, driving nails.

Dalmatian and Sam the Bulldog are playing and wrestling, rolling around on the ground.

The most God-awful, ear-piercing, terrified dog screams fill the air and everyone comes running. John dropping down from the rafters and Bruce and I from around the side of the building.

Sam's got the Dalmatian by the throat, laying on his side and is steady gathering more dog-throat into his mouth, going for the kill as is bred into 'em.

It's also bred into pit-bulls to not let go of their prey under any circumstances and John the Builder is testing that theory.

He starts by grabbing the bull-dog by his back legs and trying to pull 'em off his dog, but all that does is drag both dogs around cause Sam is latched on tight to Dalmatian's throat like he'd been born there.

Dalmatian is continually screaming non-stop, kicking

and flailing. Sam is totally limp dead-weight except for his jaws that continually move and tighten their grip.

John's starting to get real excited hearing his dog scream and seeing the blood start to trickle from his throat.

He's straddle the two bound-up dogs, kicking Sam in the nuts, jerking him up and down trying to get 'em loose.

John's prying in Sam's mouth with the claws on the back of the hammer.

No good.

John's tapping Sam on the head with the side of his hammer.

To no avail.

Dalmatian is shrieking and squealing at a higher more desperate pitch, death has 'em by the throat.

And John loses it.

And John's a tall, lanky, strong, wild man-with-a-claw-hammer as he rises from his knees, still straddling the dogs.

John has straightened his hammer to the position like you'd use it to drive a nail, his right arm stretched over his head to the limit.

John is holding Sam by the collar in his left hand as he brings the hammer down with all his might, sinking the whole front part of the hammer, to the handle, in Sam's skull, right between his blank-brown eyes.

Sam still doesn't let go.

With a yell and a grunt of great effort John brings down the hammer again on Sam's head and pulls his Dalmatian loose.

John's trembling with adrenaline and excitement, mumbling "I've killed 'em," "I've killed that dog."

Dalmatian's whimpering and moaning, scrambling away from Sam the bulldog who's laying motionless on the ground.

"I've killed 'em," John says again as we're watching.

And then Sam stands up.

And he's bleeding from his ears and his eyes and his nose, but he's standing.

And he's shaking his head a little, flinging droplets of blood around like he'd been swimming.

Then in a wobbly sort of way he trots off towards home as we stare in disbelief cause we'd seen that hammer sunk in his head twice, as hard as a man-in-panic can hit anything.

But we know he's going to die.

And we know there's probably going to be a big fight when Sam's owners catch sight of 'em, our neighbors, the Arrows family.

And they came shortly, (without Sam, he wasn't up to the trip).

And I mediated, explaining the circumstances and there was a lot of cussing and threatening but no blows or blood shed and that was that.

But we all knew we'd never see Sam again cause he was dead and just didn't know it yet.

The first thing I saw the next morning when I drove up to work was Sam chasing squirrels in the parking lot with a lot of dried blood on his dented head.

And he carried a 2-inch dent between his eyes for the four or five more years that he lived.

What finally killed that bulldog that couldn't be killed with a hammer, was a simple one-pound bag of dried lima beans that he stole from a grocery sack on the porch and carried under the house and ate.

When that sack full of dried beans got in Sam's stomach full of bull-dog juice, and started to swell, they did what a big strong mad-man with a claw hammer couldn't do.

Dog Island, Rats, Snakes, Coons

I got to observe a change in balance of the wildlife on Dog Island. When I first started going there about thirty or thirty-five years ago, there was a huge population of rats that seemed to be everywhere on the Island.

These were some kind of wood rat, and they didn't seem to be much of a problem inside the house but they were so plentiful that it was common to observe 'em scurrying from bush to bush when you'd be drinking coffee on the porch in the morning or they'd dart across the dirt roads driving back and forth to the ferry dock, even in the daytime. As kids we'd ride slow through the tall grass on the airstrip and shoot at 'em with .22s when they'd run out from under the car.

Lots of rats.

And we always had our fair share of snakes. Not an over abundance, (one or two is too many for me), but a normal amount.

Rattlesnakes, Cottonmouth Moccasins, grey and red rat snakes, black snakes, indigos, and snakes I didn't recognize.

The first change I noticed was that you didn't see nearly as many rats and there seemed to be a few more snakes.

Then it got to where you never saw a rat but the snakes were everywhere and they looked fat and healthy.

And we always had a good supply of raccoons and then their population started to boom and the snake count seemed to dwindle, finally getting down to where you rarely saw one and I didn't miss 'em much.

But the coons were the biggest pests of all cause I guess when they ate most all the snakes up, they started home-invading houses and we fought coons for years.

181

Nothing was safe from them, the would steal the fish you were fixing to clean, the watermelons out of the back of your truck, take the bait out of your boat.

So the Island went from rats to snakes, I guess because of the great food supply the rats made, then from snakes to coons. I didn't know coons ate snakes that much cause I never saw one eat a snake, but I figure the coons must have caught on to digging up snake eggs cause I know coons love eggs of all types.

We sold out and left Dog Island a few years ago and the coon population seemed to be going down hill fast, and the only thing I can attribute their demise to, is Yankees, cause their population had really increased when we left and they have the ability to make everything want to leave.

By the way, I never saw a Yankee eat a coon, just like I never saw a coon eat a snake.

It's all speculation.

Bay Scallops

There were a few around most every year. Specially east of the St. Marks Lighthouse on the grass flats. I've made a light lunch out of three or four, eaten raw, scraped from the gut and shell with a pocket knife, close to Grey Mare Rock in January.

They're delicious, sweet, a most unique delicate taste from the Gulf.

Kinda scarce, a delicacy for two or three years at the time, then they'd show up by the zillions.

All the local North Floridians and some Georgians would catch and eat and freeze all they wanted.

All the commercial fishermen of the area, the mullet fishermen, crabbers, oystermen, knew that every four to seven years a bumper crop of Bay Scallops would *"travel"* through the bay on the grass flats. They would drop everything they were doing, tie two small scallop-drags to their skiffs and harvest Bay Scallops.

All the oyster shucking houses and some of the crab picking plants would convert over-night to shucking beautiful scallop-meat, by the hundreds of gallons, to be consumed by everyone from New York to Atlanta to Miami and Mobile, a gift from Mother Nature for everybody twice a decade if you're lucky.

A shell-fish shaped just like the Shell Oil company logo, or should I say the logo is shaped from the scallop shell. An animal with dozens of blue eyes lining the perimeter of the opening in its shell, a shell-fish somewhat like an oyster or a clam except that it can move, propelling itself by jetting water, like a pump, able to move itself up into the water column, covering a lot of ground using the tidal flow, fluttering back to the grass beds like a arthritic butterfly, then moving on again if it needs to.

Extreme cycles these animals came to us on.

Not many one year.

None the next.

Quite a few the following summer.

Train loads the fourth or fifth year.

Now the State of Florida controls the supply and harvest of Bay Scallops.

Only the recreational sportsfisherman can harvest them in a special season from July 1st to September 15th, allowing just one gallon of unshucked scallops per person, or 5 gallons to the boat. (Approximately one pint of shucked scallops to the gallon).

No commercial harvest at all.

No Bay Scallops to supplement income or to feed the non-coastal world. No sharing of the bounty of Florida's Northern Gulf of Mexico with the common world or the fishermen, just to those who can afford to spend money for boats, motors, gas, ice, license, motel rooms, vacations.

They are now an absolute luxury.

But————

They are protected.

Conservation.

Limited season and harvest.

They still come the same way.

Not many one year.

None the next.

Quite a few the following summer.

Train loads the fourth or fifth year.

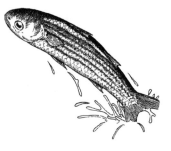

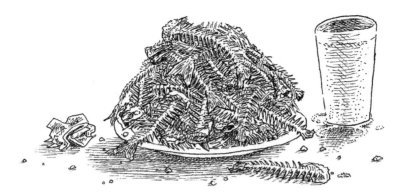

The Hippo Twins

The Hippo brothers were a pair of identical twins, reared in a small middle-Georgia farming town. They were typical good-ole-boys, always together working when they had to, knocking around and having fun every chance they got which was often.

They were big good-ole-boys as the nickname implies, the only difference in the two being absolutely identical twins was, that Little Hippo weighed in at only 405 pounds and Big Hippo topped 420. Drinking beer was a favorite pastime of theirs everyday and they'd drink at least a six-pack in the afternoon maybe two if everything was going right. Now the Hippo twin's six-packs were somewhat different than us regular folks six-packs, they considered six quarts of beer a six-pack and they could each down a quart in three or four pulls off the bottle.

The Hippo boys liked to eat as much as they liked to drink and about their favorite food was fried catfish, slaw and grits.

One nite they were coming home from a Braves game in Atlanta. They're roaring along in their old used Chrysler Imperial, windows down, discussing the ball game, drinking Budweiser by the quart, getting hungry.

Little Hippo spies an All-U-Can-Eat-Catfish special at a little creekside restaurant in Smalltown, Georgia.

Big Hippo pulls in and parks at the "Unlucky Café" without any urging.

The smells of fried catfish on the calm summer air start the Hippo boys' stomachs to rumbling, appetites heightened by all the cold beer.

Little Hippo pulls out a quarter, flips it in the air, calls tails, catches the coin, looks at it and says, "I win." With that he rolls himself out of the car door and starts strolling towards the restaurant, hitching up his pants as he walks.

Big Hippo yells out the car window "Don't take too long boy, I'm starving out here," then opens a fresh quart.

Quaint little country restaurant Little Hippo steps into. Picnic tables and benches to eat family-style on, local artwork on the walls, jukebox playing, people sitting everywhere laughing and talking and chowing down on hot fried catfish. A busy Friday night.

Little Hippo sits down at an empty table and is greeted by a friendly, smiling waitress, serving 'em some crackers and butter, asking Hippo what he wants to drink.

"Sweet tea," he says, smiling back at the lady, tearing open a pack of crackers with his teeth. "All-you-can-eat catfish, right?" he asks, popping both crackers in his mouth at once, opening another pack as he chews, "Six bucks, right?" loading butter on one cracker putting the other one on top to make a sorta garlic-butter Oreo.

"That's right, Big Boy," responds the waitress writing down his order, "bet the boss-man will lose money on you," she's saying over her shoulder, heading toward the kitchen to turn his order in.

Little Hip is happy, nodding a greeting to a pretty girl across the room, munching on a fresh scallion with one hand while he salt and peppers his slaw with the other. A cheerful, half-drunk soul anticipating his upcoming main course.

Waitress lady plops down a plate full of sizzling hot catfish with some cheese grits and hushpuppies.

Little Hip is pushing all the cracker wrappers, slaw and onions to the side, centering up that plate in front of his huge body for some serious eating, informing the waitress to tell the cook to start frying some more fish as he bites the crispy-fried tail off the catfish. While he's crunching the tail part up he's expertly pulling the meat off the backbone, stripping it perfectly on each side, shoving it into his mouth.

An eating machine he is, eating a whole catfish in two mouthfuls, three mouthfuls if you include the crispy tail part, taking a bite of hushpuppy or grits waiting on more catfish to come out, eating three plates of five catfish for a semi-total of fifteen.

"All-you-can-eat, right?" Hippo asks again as he stands up and burps.

"Right," says the waitress as she fills up his tea glass.

"Well, don't take my plate away," Little Hippo's saying as he fishes his cigarettes out of his shirt pocket, "You can take all those bones away," waving his hand over the mound of catfish skeletons and cornmeal crumbs on the table, "I'm not near thru eating but I'm going outside to smoke. I don't like people smoking indoors so I don't do it myself."

He's lighting up and inhaling deep as he walks out the door.

Little Hippo never pauses as he walks toward the Chrysler Imperial parked at the end of the lot. He's thinking about those cold Budweisers iced down in the back seat.

Before he can even reach the Chrysler, Big Hippo is getting out and lighting up a cigarette of his own.

"Man those catfish are good," says Little Hip to Big Hip, "Hurry up and eat your share cause I'm still hungry and want to go back in soon."

"Hungry?" Big Hippo quips back, "You talk about hungry, I'm about to starve to death out here smelling all that food while you're in there eating your appetizers," he's draining the last out of the quart of beer he's been sucking on, keeping his cigarette he heads for the restaurant.

The Hippo brothers have the next part of their routine down to an art form.

Big Hippo opens the door to the restaurant, turns around and blows his lung full of smoke back out the door and flicks his burnt down cigarette away. He's waltzing to his table, rubbing his hands together in excitement announcing to the waitress that he's ready for round two of the all-you-can-eat catfish marathon.

Big Hippo consumes four orders of fried catfish for a semi-total of twenty, not much bothering with the grits or hushpuppies, just the meat. Then he announces that he's going out for another smoke.

Do not take his plate, smoking settles his food and he's coming back.

They pull the smoke and switch routine two more times with Little Hippo gorging three times, Big Hip only twice but eating more fish-per-time than his identical twin brother.

As Little Hippo is paying his bill, six dollars plus tax and tea, the restaurant manager is trying to count the massive pile of catfish backbones in the kitchen, looking at Little Hippo sort-of suspicious and skeptical.

The bone-pile count is somewhere between sixty and seventy. It seems impossible that one human being (though somewhat large), can consume that many cornmeal coated, deep-fried, five to seven ounce, freshwater catfish.

Little Hippo has gone out the front door of the restaurant, heading toward the car, lighting up another cigarette, full and satisfied.

The restaurant manager is following at a short

distance, real curious.

Little Hippo's getting in the driver's side door.

Big Hippo's kinda snoozing, mouth hanging open, pants and belt buckle undone for more comfort, feeling the full effects from the thirty or so catfish and the quarts of Bud.

Little Hip is cranking up the Imperial when a flashlight is stuck in the window and there sit the Hippo Twins, all eight hundred and twenty-five pounds of 'em plus the catfish.

"Alright, get out and get up some money you conniving, thieving, gluttonous hogs, pay up or go to jail," demands the observant restaurant man. "I'm calling the law unless you boys cough up forty dollars." "I knew no one man could eat that many catfish and live, not counting the grits, crackers and slaw." "Pay up and pay up quick and without a word or I'll have you both locked up, my brother-in-law is a deputy and he's on duty tonite."

Big Hippo's like a deer caught in the headlights, waking up from his Budweiser and catfish induced coma. Little Hip is digging in his pockets, counting out the cash.

Money in hand, the restaurant man is telling the Hippo Brothers to get out and never come back.

Little Hippo is backing out and following the man's orders to leave as fast as he can cause the high sheriff in the county has dealt with the Hippo Twins before.

Realizing that they're not gonna have to go to jail they open a new quart each of Budweiser in celebration, and point that ole Chrysler Imperial down the road toward their next new adventure.

Old Blanket

Funny things mean a lot to me.

For example -

Tonite I'm getting down an old, old wool blanket. Lime grey-green in color, kinda ragged around the edges.

Just spreading it out on the bed makes me feel warmer but suddenly, it makes me feel a lot older too.

I had unfolded that old blanket many times, for many years and all of a sudden I'd just realized how many years it has been. Realized how many times and how many different conditions I'd unfolded that blanket in.

Most of the twenty-five years I'd been associated with it (the blanket), I was wrapped up in it where I am now, between mullet-fishing trips, in room #3 of the old motel at Spring Creek, snatching a few hours sleep between tides.

A place with a bathroom, a bed, four walls and a door. A space heater to keep the temperature above the freezing mark.

True comfort, almost like home.

Tonite is January 1, 2002. It's cold, damp and raining, thirty-eight degree weather on the coast.

Miserable.

That's why the good ole 100% wool, who knows where it came from or how old it is, heat-trapping, face warming, toe saving, green-grey blanket is going on the bed.

Now I remember the ACE again and the winter nights offshore, when I'd be spreading this blanket on one of the bunks on the boat. Shivering cold and damp clear thru to the bones from two days of grouper and amberjack fishing in January. Tired from anchoring and re-anchoring twenty times that day, catching fish, gutting fish, packing fish, cutting bait, rinsing blood off the deck, tired from trying to keep your balance all day, tired from having to hold the frying pan on the stove in the pitching and rocking seas just to cook supper.

A long, wet, chilly and nasty day.

Supper's been cooked, drinks have been drunk. Time to go to bed with the dampness soaked clear thru to your innards.

The moldy pillows come out. The sleeping bags are unrolled and all the clothes, bedding, books, blankets and junk that have been crammed under the bow-cap of the ACE get divided out to the two or three crew members on board.

I always got the green blanket.

It was mine.

I had inherited it when we bought Spring Creek Restaurant and Motel back in 1977. The blanket came with the motel and I had "borrowed" it for a three-day trip one winter on the ACE.

I put it back in the motel, in the room I kept for myself, ten years later after I'd sold the boat.

I'd never even thought of the significance of that old wool blanket till I spread it on my bed for the thousandth time in January 2002.

The children I'd wrapped up in it, sons, nieces, nephews.

The pillows it had made rolled-up.

The legs it had covered on winter trips to Dog Island, my wife, sister-in-laws, mother, mother-in-law.

The severe weather conditions I'd slept or tried to sleep, wrapped up in it.

The bugs I'd shaken out of it.

The mildew that occasionally grew on it.

The comfort I'd gotten out of that old piece of woolen fabric.

That blanket still does the job. It has never failed even though it was damp most the time from the water leaking through the scuttle hole, from the fog seeping into the cabin of the ACE, from the general moisture that permeates the air on an offshore boat.

It kept me warm enough not to shiver, at least letting my bones warm up some, if not my toes, on those winter fishing trips. Warm enough to make daylite, coffee and more fish.

That 100% loyal wool is hard to beat.

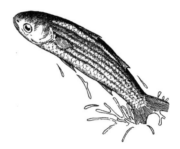

I Wasn't Worth a Hoot At Night

I hate to admit it but I wasn't really very good at catching mullet at night.

I tried hard to catch 'em. I couldn't help but try to catch a load after watching all the other gill-net fishermen come in with tripped-on loads of mullet. Me stuck running the restaurant, from 6 to 10 p.m.. and just dying to get in my mullet skiff and hunt me up a bunch.

I caught fish real good in the daytime. I had taught myself to see fish pretty well, even though they wouldn't be "showing" much, I could spot 'em and catch 'em.

But night fishing is different, specially on real dark nights when you've got no moon. Then it is sounds instead of sights that you have to clue in on. If I had known then, what I do now, I would of caught boat loads at nite but I was still in the learning phase. Had I known that when I'd hear a single mullet make that "flipping" sound, a noise made by the fish just barely squirting out of the water, fluttering his tail and fins and plopping back down with a small splash, was caused by that particular fish being squeezed out of a vast school of mullet silently swimming by in the dark. If I had known that, I would have struck that noise and loaded down.

But I didn't.

I wanted to hear a bunch of fish sloshing and jumping before I'd strike.

I know now that a million pound school of fish will glide right by your boat, without making so much as a ripple.

Sometimes I'd sit on a run stand all night without making a strike and as soon as it was light enough to see I'd spy a good bunch, round 'em up with the 600 yards of net I carried and have a good catch, wondering why no fish had come by during the night.

They had been. Streaming by all night, I just hadn't known what to listen for.

We had a few good catches at night but we used a different tactic to locate the fish. We would run the shoreline when it was black-dark and constantly be shining a high powered spotlight out ahead of the boat and off to the sides. When that bright beam of light would cross over a big school of mullet it would make the fish hop and jump and skip across the water looking like a great pan of popcorn with hundreds of fish in the air.

We would quickly shut the light off when those mullet would show like that, and then we'd take in the area that the fish were jumping in the thickest, making a big circle with three to four hundred yards of our net and putting the rest of the net out in the center of the circle. We would turn that spotlight back on once we had deployed our net and watch the circled-up fish try to tear the net down in their panic, trying to escape that bright light.

All in all I just didn't have the knowledge to really catch a lot of fish at night.

But I could wear 'em out in the daytime and I finally devoted all my energy to that, figuring it wouldn't hurt to get a little sleep once in a while.

198

A Pine in the Rain

I was sitting in our pine grove in Middle Georgia, leaning against one of the fourteen year old trees that grew in that forty acre part of the farm.

I was trying to trick an old gobbler on that spring morning, but this story is about trees not turkeys.

The pines were planted in rows, each tree in the row five feet apart, each row eight feet wide.

They had grown well in the soil of the old peach and apple orchards that used to be there, wheat, peanuts and cotton had followed the fruit trees, and now the pines reaping the benefits of the well worked soil and the nutrients and minerals left over from growing those previous crops.

Anyway it started to rain.

And the trees were about thirty-five feet tall and canopied completely.

Everybody knows what a pine tree looks like.

With its skinny green needles pointing toward the sky and its thin scaly branches angled always upward, each branch connecting to the tapered trunk, that's covered in a thick brown bark patterned like the cracked and creased bed of a dried-up lake, the trunk getting larger and the bark getting thicker as it goes into the ground, feeding the stump and the roots.

A grand design.

A design to water that tree to all advantage when it rains, even a light rain like of that morning.

And it had been a dry-dry season.

But when it had been a light steady rain just for a few minutes, I started hearing a hissing sound, soft, barely audible, you could almost feel it, more than hear it.

And you notice the tree you're leaning against, the little bubbles appearing in places on the trunk, oozing out from the bark.

You start looking hard to see what's going on and you see a dampness and in some places a trickle of water and you follow it up the tree and realize that in this lightest of rain, the moisture hitting those thousands of thin needles runs down the needle, transferring the water to the branches that are angled right, that pass the water on to the trunk, that guides the water to the roots through the channels in the bark and as it starts its rush to the ground and gains volume and speed near the stump it must force air out of the tiny cracks in the bark that make the hissing sound and the bubbles.

An irrigation system for each tree.

A system to gather and direct even the slightest amount of water to the place needed most, to the stump, where the roots can suck it up and send it back through its veins to the upper reaches of the limbs.

Well thought out design and engineering.

Needs no modification.

Wonder who thought that up.

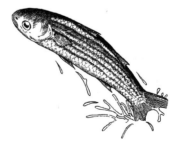

202

Momma

Momma, what can I say about you?

I can't say too much. There's not enough paper, ink, or love in all-the-world-combined to put it down in words.

You've always been there, I'll name just a few times.

There to pull my '58, wood-floored, banged up, but always ran good, Kharmen-Ghia-VW, out of the woods on Lakeshore Drive, when me and the boys took the curve too fast.

I don't think you even told Daddy.

There to pull the handbrake on the '52 Chevy, with both hands, hard enough to stop us on the steep hill coming down to U.S. 27 and save our lives when the brakes went out.

To blast the six-foot rattlesnakes outta the yard when we were playing.

Beat the moccasins with a hoe or a broom the year the snakes got so bad on Lake Jackson.

To and from ball practice, always praising, always positive, cheering us on even when we fouled-up.

Always beautiful, always elegant.

During hurricanes, baseball games, plays, ballets, hard times, broke times, good times, sickness, tragedy, births, deaths, poison-ivy, two-hundred red-bugs, driving for the first-time, cooking fish and game, our tears, fears and scares, no matter what, you were always there.

You'll always be there.

With your love and caring and your constant passion of wanting to help others and trying to help others, no matter how hopeless the cause.

And you helped a lot.

Especially me, or us, your children. You instilled in us a strong binding love and importance of family and loyalty. It's in the gene pool.

You've been a shining star on a cloudy nite as faithful as the sunrise. Unstoppable as a full-moon tide when your hard-headedness kicks in.

That's in the gene pool too.

Your compassion, patience, love and devotion to family were exemplified by the care of Mammaw, your mother, and Grandma Helen, your mother-in-law who you kept in your home for 10 years.

The great recipes you created out of necessity, like your hushpuppies at the restaurant, concocted at a bream-fry at my house when we didn't have enough cornmeal.

The famous "House Dressing of Spring Creek", the stuffed tomatoes, the sweet and sour sauces, chocolate peanut-butter pie.

You'll always be there.

In the decisions we make.

The help we give.

The love we share to the foods we eat.

You can't get away from us.

Your influence was too great and we love you too much to let you go far.

You'll always be there.

This beautiful poem was found by my father, in my
mother's jewelry box, a few months after she died.

A much needed message from his wife of fifty-two years.

> May God keep and comfort you
> And softly ease your sorrow
> And may you feel His presence near
> Through every new tomorrow.

> Carolyn Rose Brooks Lovel
> May 2002
> April 25, 1932 - May 14, 2002

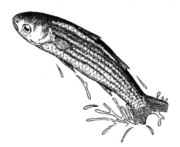

The Speed of the Moon

It's mid-August in Middle Georgia.

Comfortable, cool, no bugs, about 11 p.m.

At the High Hill above the cabin is an Oak tree. Just a Red Oak, young as Red Oaks go, maybe about sixty years old.

But it grew on the high part of the hill, over-looking the Flint River basin for miles.

And in August, on the full moon, a blistering white-light from the east, would break over the bluff and climb from the base to the tip-top branches of that Red Oak tree.

And that full moon is moving right along.

So fast you can't take your eyes off of it as the tip-top of the round full moon pops its gleam over a branch, then a leaf, then another branch and leaf, like a brilliant spotlite being slowly but steadily scanned along the branches from bottom to top.

It's a quick trip when you've got something to mark it on.

Slow, but constant and never stopping.

Remarkable to look at.

Time going by so slow and steady that it seems like forever.

But really it's quick cause it never ever stops, steady, steady, steady.

Watching the speed of the moon rise through that oak every August makes it hard to believe it's August again.

High School Football

High School football was great to me.

I loved it.

It was a time to get geared-up with all the pads, gang-up with all your good high school buddies and try to tear each other apart.

It's one of the only times in your life you could turn yourself loose, I mean completely loose, to focus all your energy, your emotion, all your attention on one play, one assignment. To run over somebody or try too.

To get low, put your head down, charge like a bull and go thru somebody.

Man it felt good.

All the crashing and grunting and growling and pushing and beating till a whistle blew then we'd get up and go do it again from a different direction.

My favorite play was a plain old dive play, hand me the ball straight up the middle. Really a trap play was even better. One of the guards would pull out and flatten an unsuspecting defensive tackle giving me time to build up more speed before hitting the linebacker.

I remember one time at practice the quarterback called a dive play to pound the defense at the core.

The quarterback takes the snap.

I'm bent low with my arms shaped to take the hand-off.

The ball's slapped into my belly and secured by my arms and I'm screaming thru the middle of the line, literally screaming with an attack-animal growl like a wolf or a bulldog makes before he bites you.

The hole between center and guard is open and I'm blowing thru it wide-open.

Three yards from scrimmage I meet one of my best buddies, Vince, a linebacker and he is roaring in to close the hole and we meet at teenage testosterone fired, killer-instinct velocity, head-on. There's explosions in both our helmets.

The first thing I remember is our coach, Coach Flowers. He has me, by my face-guard, in one of his hands and Vince, by the faceguard, in the other hand. He's jerking us up by our heads and shaking our heads and screaming to the rest of the team, "That's what I'm talking about," "That's what I want," "Intensity!" "Intensity!" "You give me that and we'll win it all."

Me and Vince are staggering around, we're loopy, dazed trying to find the right huddle to go back to, both brain-addled but proud at laying a hard lick on each other like that.

I loved it.

My face-guard was broken and sticking in my neck but I didn't care. All I wanted was another helmet and for the quarterback to call my number again.

I'll never forget playing against my first black-boy.

It had always been white-on-white until they brought Keith onto the team. A fine fellow he was too. Smart, classy, a real nice guy and one heck of an athlete.

At this particular time they had me playing linebacker on defense.

Keith's lining up at tailback on offense and they run a sweep, pitching the ball to Keith coming around my side of the field.

I pick the play up and charge in to make the tackle, lining up on the new black-boy to stick 'em good, rattle his teeth and welcome 'em to the team. He's dead in front of me and my arms are going around 'em, I'm fixing to knock his socks off and throw 'em for a loss.

But I never touched 'em, much less tackled 'em, I hit the ground alright, but alone.

That boy put a move on me like I'd never seen. He kinda shook to the left with part of his body and that left me tackling that way cause he disappeared to the right leaving me digging up grass while he went on to the end zone.

This event left me much more wary and giving Keith a lot more space the next time he got the ball.

It became a brand new game when there was more than just white-boys playing.

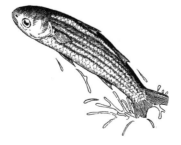

Skunk Attack

Rooster and Darlene are like family to us in Middle Georgia.

They are people of the finest kind and they have just finished building their dream-house on a high-hill, overlooking beautiful green rolling pasture with their cows and calves grazing on it. There are cotton fields and planted pines just as far as the eye can see.

Daylight is just breaking and Rooster and Darlene are sipping their first cup of coffee, sitting on their new sofa, looking out through their new windows at the beginnings of a peaceful, serene, gorgeous Sunday morning.

Not quite.

Rooster sniffs real deep a couple of times and asks, "Darlene, (sniff, sniff) you smell something?"

Darlene says, "Rooster I've been smelling something and hoped it was my imagination."

The smell is starting to get thick so I'm told, so thick that you started to taste it.

Darlene walks to the door on the west side of the house and goes outside and announces that she doesn't smell anything out there.

Rooster walks out the front door onto the porch and sniffs and says he doesn't smell anything out there either.

But Rooster hears something.

An unusual sound, a high-pitched scratchy-squeally sound coming from around the corner of the house.

Rooster goes to investigate, rounds the corner of the house and discovers the root of the problem.

Piled up against the side of his central heat and air-conditioning unit are two amorous, odorous, baby-making skunks, engaged in reproduction, missionary style.

Rooster yells to Darlene, "Get my gun, get my gun

quick," while he keeps an eye on the critters.

Darlene brings Rooster a pistol. Hoping for his .38 he gets a .22, but he guesses that will do as he approaches the oblivious skunks to a distance of two feet.

Taking careful aim Rooster shoots the top skunk (the male) and this causes the skunk to jerk and spray musk but he still keeps doing his duty. Rooster swears that he saw the lady skunk's little black paws reach around the old boar-skunk's neck, and hold 'em down good and tight, after he shot 'em the first time.

"Bam," Rooster shoots the skunk again and both skunks jump up and bolt down their nesting hole they've burrowed under Rooster's central A/C unit.

Rooster's in the heat of battle now, he's been coated in musk and the fight is on to the end. He lays down so he can stick his arm in the skunk burrow and fires all his bullets into it.

The skunks bolt out of their emergency exit on the other side of the unit and go running under the main house, disappearing into the gloom and dark, doing their defensive-thing as they go, laying out a thick cloud of scent, filling the air inside and outside with it.

There's no other choice but to go after the perpetrator on hands and knees in the crawl-space under the house and Rooster knows he needs an assistant to shine the light while he carries the now reloaded gun.

Rooster has Darlene call Mr. Luddy Bumkin. Mr. Luddy's been working for Rooster's family since Rooster was born and Rooster is fifty-two.

Mr. Luddy says, "Mr. Rooster suh, I is too old to be crawlin' and chasin' under that house, I don't believe I'd be much help."

"Go get some help," Rooster instructs, "and be quick about it," he says, ready to take the battle to the vile beasts that have ruined his peaceful morning.

Mr. Luddy returns about thirty minutes later with Thirteen.

Not thirteen people or thirteen helpers but with Thirteen, who was the boy-child born after the twelfth child, when all the names had been used up and they couldn't think what to call 'em.

Thirteen's paycheck read: PAYABLE to <u>Thirteen,</u> that's his name.

Its' still early on a Sunday morning and Thirteen's as drunk as any man can be and still walk, except when he falls down.

But Thirteen's willing and ready to go knowing Rooster always pays 'em well for his services. He's still dressed in his Saturday night party clothes which are a black nylon Nike running suit and black patent-leather pointy toe shoes with no socks.

Rooster has handed thirteen a flashlight and they're both crawling side-by-side under the house hunting skunks.

The air is thick with excited skunk juice.

The flashlite is shining back and forth at Rooster's direction, they're steady crawling, further and further, searching.

"Suh," Thirteen says, "Suh, I sees 'em over by de fireplace suh."

Now Thirteen's got a "Suh" thing. He say Sir or Suh, before he starts the sentence and after the sentence.

"Suh, dey bunched up together suh."

Rooster see the staring green eyes in the gloom, takes aim and fire a few rounds into the fragrant ball of skunks.

One skunk falls and the other runs off.

"Get that dead skunk Thirteen," Rooster yells.

"Suh, yes suh," "I gets 'em suh," Thirteen says as he crawls past Rooster, holding the light on that dead skunk.

Rooster told me he had never witnessed the actual spray cloud emitted by the animal, but that he has now, first-hand and close-up. Lit by the flashlite in Thirteen's hand.

Thirteen has crawled past Rooster, his patent leather

feet are about even with Rooster's head. He's got that flashlite beam fixed hard on the skunk, almost in reaching distance.

A thick, wet, vaporous, encompassing cloud emits from the skunk lying on the ground, enveloping Thirteen and drifting on to Rooster.

Rooster told me he heard Thirteen sorta gasp, and then gag and cough and gag some more.

The flashlite goes flying and bouncing across the ground, thrown from Thirteen's hand. His down-pointed, pointy-toe patent leather shoes that have been crawling and pushing 'em under the house across that hard clay ground, suddenly turn straight-up. Thirteen clasps his arms across his chest like a corpse in a casket and starts rolling and spinning faster than an Olympic skater in her tightest twirls on the ice, rolling like an out-of-control black log towards the opening from under the house.

"Stop Thirteen Stop," Rooster's yelling as he rolls by 'em like a whirlwind, those pointed shoes spinning round and round like clock-hands gone wild. "Stop and get your flashlite or I'll shoot you instead of that skunk!" he threatens but to no avail, cause Thirteen's yelling as he's rolling, "Suh dat skunk's done parfumed me suh, done parfumed me in da face suh," and rolls right out from under the house and keeps on rolling down the pasture till he's stopped by the fence.

Mr. Luddy Bumkins gets Thirteen up, hands 'em another flashlite and puts 'em back under the house skunk stalking.

The skunk Rooster had shot is laying up against the base of the fireplace where he had been.

"Get that one and take 'em out," Rooster orders.

"Suh, yes suh," Thirteen says, crawling with the flashlite in his left hand reaching the dead skunk.

Rooster said he saw Thirteen reach up with his right hand and grab the skunk by the neck and the skunk started jumping and thrashing and spraying. Thirteen drops the flashlite in his left hand, still holding the skunk with his right, and reaches up with both hands and Rooster hears a cracking crunching noise as Thirteen breaks the skunk's neck.

"Suh," Thirteen says, "Suh, he weren't dead when I gots here suh, be he be dead now suh."

Now Rooster can hear Mr. Bumkin yelling from out in the yard, "Here he Mr. Rooster," "Here he Mr. Rooster," "Here be de other skunk runnin' round de yard," "Here he, here he!"

The other skunk is running around and around the yard, darting and spraying and finally taking refuge by holing-up under the air conditioning unit where the battle began.

Rooster, Thirteen and the broke-neck-shot skunk are out from under the house and in hot pursuit of the number two skunk.

The escape-exit hole from the burrow has been blocked off.

Thirteen's got a shovel and is digging the entry hole wider.

Rooster's laying on the ground, peering into the skunk's den, firing a few rounds in the hole.

Thirteen spots the skunk back at the blocked escape exit and says, "Suh, suh, I can see 'em suh," but the animal is where Rooster can't get a shot from that side.

"You watch 'em from back there and I'm gonna fire in the front and you tell me if I get 'em."

Rooster lays down flat on his back and extends his arm as far as it will go into the skunk hole and fires all his bullets.

"Did I get 'em?" Rooster asks.

"Suh, no suh," Thirteen replies sounding depressed.

Rooster's reloading for another volley, then laying down and firing again.

"How bout that time?" Rooster asks with hope in his voice.

"Suh, no suh," Thirteen replies again sadly, standing up and gagging and coughing, laying his head on his arms, as he's leaning against a fence post saying, "Suh, I done been parfumed so much I'm feeling sick suh," but takes a few deep breaths and goes back to the task at hand, blocking and guarding the exit hole.

Rooster says to Thirteen, "I'll get 'em this time," and lays down and puts his arm shoulder and all in the hole firing all his bullets.

"Did I get 'em that time Thirteen?"

No reply is needed.

The look on Thirteen's face is the answer.

His eyes are closed, there's a big pearly-white smile on his face and he's looking at the sky giving thanks.

"Suh, yes suh," "You gots 'em that time suh."

Rooster's got a picture of Thirteen standing there with a wad of cash money in his left hand and two dead skunks in his right hand.

I'm glad I missed out on that hunting trip. That was one of those trips when the animal could fire back.

Note: This story was sorta funny for a while, til the scent continued to get stronger and more skunks were removed from the duct work. Then it wasn't funny anymore. Before it was over with, Rooster, Darlene and family had to move out of their brand-new house. They had to replace the entire air conditioning system, both units. They had to have all new duct work put in. Remove carpets, rugs, clothes and curtains because of the scent.

About the time they had to move out of the house, there ceased to be any more humor in this situation.

Home Invaders

It was about three o'clock on a Sunday afternoon, two days before the close of Spring Gobbler season. All of a sudden my schedule was free and I could get to our river cabin in middle Georgia and hunt.

I arrived at our remotely located cabin in the woods about eight or eight-thirty in the evening. It's an absolutely beautiful evening and I'm soaking in the coolness, the quietness, listening to the crickets and the frogs, watching the first fire-flies start to blink.

Well it's time to start opening the cabin up. Turning on the well, lighting the hot water heater, getting things in order before black-dark.

I grab my satchel in one hand, my keys and overnite bag in the other and walk up on the porch. As I'm strolling by our bedroom windows that face out on the porch, I notice that our nice, white Levelor blinds, that shade our windows, are hanging in shreds like someone had taken a machete to 'em.

I stop, stare at those shredded blinds for a second and immediately know, some wild critter is in the house.

I drop my bags and run back to my truck, snatching my Speedmaster .22 rifle out from under the seat and run back.

I peer in all the windows and I can't see anything.

I can't hear anything moving inside.

All the doors are locked.

It's getting dark, all quiet except for the natural nite sound and the low roar of the river.

It's too dark to see anything inside the house as I put my key into the front door lock that opens into the main room of the cabin.

I start easing the door open with the rifle barrel, wanting the muzzle of that gun to go in the house first.

It's hard to get the door to open up wide enough to

walk in cause there's so much broken glass and debris on the floor but I shove it open anyway expecting anything - the safety's off, on my rifle.

All is deathly quiet.

But all is certainly not right.

The house is a shamble, a wreck.

Just from where I'm standing inside the front door, and as dim as the light is, the amount of damage I can see at a quick glance is incredible. But I'm not yet concerned with the damage.

I want to know what's in here.

I have to walk all the way across the room to turn on the lights, and I'm crunching thru broken glass and stepping over spilled furniture with every step.

I see a dark mass laying in the middle of the hall and I'm focused on that. Then I recognized what it is, a big bird, a big black bird sprawled out, obviously dead.

I turn on the lights, still looking and listening, wary and spooked, and gaze down at a dead buzzard.

I click the safety back on my rifle.

Then I notice that something has eaten every bit of that dead buzzard but feathers, bones and beak.

I click the safety back off on my rifle and wonder what kind of Stephen King movie I'm in.

Now I'm no longer concerned about the dead buzzard that's been consumed so thoroughly that he's not messy or doesn't even stink. I'm worried about what ate 'em up.

I turn on the bedroom lights and there it is.

Another buzzard.

And he's dead too but he's fresh and whole. Probably died of panic cause he'd had plenty to eat, he looked fat to me, eating his house-mate like he did.

I carried the two dead buzzards out, came back in the house, turned all the lights on to assess the damage.

One quick look and the first thing I had to do was pour me a strong rum drink.

What those birds did to the inside of that house was unbelievable. You couldn't have hired a bunch of thugs to go wreck somebody's house, that could have done any better job.

To begin the description of destruction I'll start with my trophy wild turkey that I had stuffed, full size, twelve-inch beard, inch and a half spurs. He was laying on his back with one wing pulled off and all his breast feathers ripped out, looking very disturbed.

Our tri-pod mounted telescope had been knocked over onto my new CD player, breaking both instruments to pieces.

Every vase and bowl and ornament on the mantle over the fireplace was knocked down and broken.

All our Audubon plates, displayed so nicely on the wall were in pieces on the floor, the chairs tipped over and scattered around the dining room table, the light fixtures in the ceiling bent and twisted almost catching the house on fire when I turned them on.

The linens were pulled out of the cabinets, the kitchen counters were swept clean of their goods, coffee canister, tea canister, sugar canister, all glass, were broken and scattered along with their contents. Hand-me-down family china cups and bowls were smashed or chipped, stuffing pulled out of pillows on the beds and couches.

All the dolls on display had been attacked, some were saved, some were not.

And to top it all off everything in the house, the sofa, the sink, the floors and counter tops, dressers, tables and chairs, everything, looked like somebody with a bucket of white paint had used a large brush and slung that white paint everywhere.

Every wall and window was scratched and clawed from those frantic birds trying to get out.

They came down the chimney.

That's the only way they could have come, all the doors and windows were closed and locked. The fireplace screen was blown out into the middle of the living room.

I call my neighbors, my good friends living on the 100 acres next door and tell 'em to come over, I want to show 'em something they won't believe.

Mr. Ben and his wife come right over.

They come inside and their eyes get wide, their mouths fall open.

"Call the law," Mr. Ben says, "call the law now, they've got to catch who ever did this."

I tell Mr. Ben not to worry about that, that I've already got 'em, and that there was two of 'em, and that they are all piled up outside, dead.

"Come on, I'll show 'em to you," I say as I head out that way. His eyes really get big and he's a little reluctant to follow but I'm already stomping off into the dark in the direction of my truck under the tree.

Mr. Ben's coming but he's not hurrying, I think he was a little bit leery about what he was fixing to see, him still thinking humans were responsible.

"Well I'll be," he says, "Buzzards," and he looks at them and looks at me and starts to laugh a little and I start to laugh cause there's not much else to do.

We're all back in the house now, shaking our heads, chuckling, out right laughing at the total out-right mess everything is in.

I took a bunch of pictures, but when I got 'em developed and looked at 'em one time I threw 'em straight in the garbage. I didn't want to see it or remember it.

I slept on the porch that night, it was a lot nicer outside than inside.

The next day I moved all the furniture out on the porches. We took all the upholstered stuff to the dump. I called a professional cleaning crew to do a scrub-down of the inside and they send the manager out to assess the job and see how many people and what type of supplies they need.

After he had surveyed the damage for a while, and asked me all the questions about the invaders, and made his notes on what and who he needed, I had to ask him a question.

I ask Mr. Professional Clean-up Man if this wasn't the worst job he had ever had to do.

He immediately answered "no." This wasn't nearly the worst clean-up he and his crew had been involved with. Then he proceeded to tell me about that clean-up.

He said that the City of Thomaston had a main sewer line that was continually stopping up, backing up sewage, causing all sorts of problems for the city. They had trouble locating the stoppage and when they did find it they had to use heavy equipment to dig up the line and unclog it.

The problem was so bad that the city spent $200,000.00 on a special truck, that had a tank and a big air compressor. Now instead of locating the blockage and digging it up, they could just hook a big hose in the end of the sewer line, build up a bunch of pressure in the tank and blow the obstruction out of the line.

Sounds simple and efficient.

Well sure enough a week or so after the purchase of the new, high-tech, blow-the-line-out truck, the sewer lines stopped up.

The City Sewer Department brings their new machine to where they can access the main sewer line and they hook her up.

And they fire off their big compressor and they start building up pressure in the tank, and they build it up and build it up, watching the gauge till they've got about a billion pounds of pressured air ready to release.

The city crew turns that clog-busting burst of air loose, thinking that this is truly the way to go.

What they didn't think about was the nice big subdivision of homes that were at the end of that clogged sewer line.

That pressurized air cleared the line alright. It cleared everybody's sewer lines by blasting every bit of the contents of every sewer line connected to all those nice homes back out the drains they came from. The force was so great that the liquid and semi-liquid, (we all know what's in any given sewer pipe) blew out hard enough to stick it on the ceilings. Every kitchen sink, bathtub, bathroom sink and toilet regurgitated its contents with a vengeance, coating every thing and every body.

Can you imagine if you were taking a shower or sitting on the commode when this event took place?

Mr. Professional Clean-up Man told me they had to go rent hazardous-waste suits, with helmets and respirators from Atlanta, for the crews to wear while they removed the "stuff" from the walls, ceiling and floors of the outraged homeowners' houses.

He said my job just called for rubber gloves and normal household cleaners.

I felt a lot better after that.

By the way that crew did a jam-up job on our place, leaving it cleaner and shinier than ever, seeing how they scrubbed it with brushes from ceiling to floor and all the wood furniture too.

Interesting note:

We debated about how and why those buzzards came down my chimney, especially why two of 'em came down and I think I found the answer.

An elderly South Georgia farmer was eating dinner in our restaurant one night and he had heard about our buzzard break-in. He called me over and asked me if I had ever seen a buzzard's nest.

Now I've spent a lot of time in the woods and now that he mentioned it, I could not recall ever seeing one, had not even though about it really.

And he told me I probably would not ever see one, cause buzzards make their nests down inside old hollow trees and in old abandoned chimneys. He told me he had some old tenant houses on his place and that the birds nested in the chimneys there.

I can tell you this. A buzzard with a blow-torch can't get in my chimney now, with the bird-proof contraption I had built up there.

A good friend of mine that lives in the middle of Taylor county said that he didn't think he wanted to move to the north part of the county, where Rooster's and my place are. After the problems we had he thought the buzzards and the skunks were too mean to live up there with.

Another interesting note:

Guess how my expensive home-owner's insurance policy read, "No damage covered due to rodents, insects or birds."

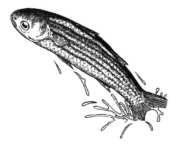

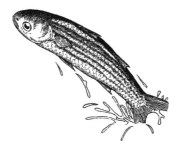

Bugs

Being located on this beautiful coastline of the Gulf of Mexico where the oaks, pines and palmettos grow right down to the marsh grass, able to survive this salt environment from all the freshwater that holds up in our swamps and flows out of the ground, we are also blessed with every kind of insect there is on earth.

We got 'em all. You name 'em, we got 'em, every type of bug that crawls or flies. Some of 'em don't bite, but unfortunately, most of ours do.

Here's some of my favorites listed somewhat in order of irritability.

Sand Gnats

Probably the most persistent biting and most plentiful of our blood-sucking bugs. The pest I find most irritating on a constant basis. Get so thick at times that you can't breathe, except through your nose cause if you open your mouth you'll inhale a hundred and almost choke to death. Marsh grass is a 100% indicator of their presence. Warm, foggy spring mornings will bring them around you in a cloud like smoke, filling your hair, chewing your scalp, eating the inside of your ears out, irritating every piece of exposed flesh with their burning-itching bites.

Mosquitoes

Have them by the thousands at times cause of all the freshwater that lays still in the swamps, but you can escape them with screens and repellents. The buzzing noise in your ears while you're trying to sleep is worse than their bite.

Yellow Flies

The most painful biter and the sneakiest. You don't know this demon is in the area until it feels like someone drove a nail in your elbow. They are quick, hard to kill and will bite you more than one time each. The wound they make usually itches like mad and swells immensely. Luckily we only get them by the hundreds and they only stay a few weeks.

Deer Flies

Somewhat like yellow flies except smaller and brown spotted. They are a lot slower fliers and you can feel it when they light on you, so they are easy to slap and kill, but they still get in quite a few bites because they attack in clouds, swarming and buzzing around you so thick that you resemble "Pig Pen" in the Peanuts comic strip.

Dog Flies

Looks just like common house flies with the exception that they love bare legs and have a sharp painful bite that leaves small whelps. Usually the flies don't bother you till noon to one o'clock in the day. They seem to show up one at a time but at a constant rate all day, till there's hundreds on your boat, sixty miles offshore, by three o'clock in the afternoon. One of the painful side effects of Dog Fly attacks are the self-inflicted injuries given to bare legs by the little round metal tabs on the top of baseball caps, cause you are constantly snatching it off your head and slapping flies on your legs. Sometimes the fly-bite doesn't hurt as bad as the attempted fly killing.

Horseflies

Big green-eyed colorful flies. Dozens of varieties and sizes. Buzz you a lot in summer and fall, usually only one or two or three at a time. Don't bite often but is painful when they do. They take a big bite out of you.

Redbugs or Chiggers

If you are in the woods you are in their territory. A double-canopied hardwood hammock with palmetto patches and some cabbage palms scattered around seems to abound with them. A few can be picked up anywhere but on occasion people must have stepped in "nests" of them. As many as two hundred festering redbug bites have been reported per leg, causing much misery and doctor's treatment. A home treatment is to put fingernail polish on each bite and suffocate the embedded bug to death. It is recommended to use the same colored polish every day or else it could be embarrassing if you have to seek professional treatment and show the infected area, displaying multi-colored dots from your beltline down. Unnerves the physician at first sight.

Ticks

Seem to enjoy the same habitat as redbugs so it's possible to acquire both species at the same time. We seem to have a wide variety of types and sizes. The seed tick being the most difficult to remove, burying his little head deep in your skin and being so small to try to grab ahold of to pull out. A few dozen can take a lot of time to remove especially those on your back. An unexpected deer tick found in the thick hair behind your ear can sometimes be exciting specially when it's as big as the end of your finger and you didn't know it was there. Don't mash 'em too hard trying to pick 'em out or you'll ruin your clothes, the carpet and whatever piece of upholstered furniture you're sitting on. A tick that size holds about a half-pint of black-looking blood and he's about to bust anyway he's so full.

Scorpions

Really seem to like pinewoods and deep-pile carpets, where when stepped on, it feels similar to having an ice-pick stuck in the bottom of your foot. Have been known to ride fresh bed linens off the clothes-line and be made up in the bed to awaken you after midnite with a shot in the left cheek of your rear end. Not many of those pests to worry about, a dozen or so spotted each year. Won't kill you. The suffering no worse than a wasp or a hornet.

Yellow Jackets

Dangerous bugs if you happen to disturb their nests, which is usually in the ground and if you happen to run over it with a lawnmower they will be in a swarm over you faster than you can realize what's happened and run away from 'em. You never escape without a few stings. We recorded a high of thirty-two stings on my little brother Kenny when he blew apart a Yellow Jacket nest mowing with Mammaw's Snapper. His thirty second bite came after we got Brother Kenny in the house and he scratched his curly hair and a single yellow jacket fell out and bit 'em on the end of his nose. Yellow Jackets can wind up stinging you in places rarely visited by other insects, like on your tongue or the inside of your cheek. The way this happens is when the bug crawls into your Pepsi can, after the sugar, and you take a big old swallow and boom, you're bit, before you can spit 'em out. I've known this to happen many times.

Wasps

Of the many species and sub-species, we have them all. Pygmy wasp, Guinea wasps, the big Red Wasps. The Red Wasp seems to be the most prevalent, their honey comb type nest commonly seen built under the eaves of houses but they build plenty of nests in bushes and trees, specially around lakes and rivers. I once witnessed two guys in a canoe try to kill a snake that was laying on a log in the river. The guy in front of the canoe was going to whack the snake with the blade of his paddle, slicing his weapon through a swamp-myrtle bush hanging over the water. In the process he sliced the end of a wasps nest that was the size of a small pizza, instantly inspiring hundreds of angry wasps into battle, attacking the two boys in the canoe mercilessly, stinging each repeatedly, driving both into the water to join the large cottonmouth moccasin they had managed to scare off his log. Every time they'd stick their head out of the water the wasps attacked it. When they'd duck under the water they'd think about the snake and try to come out of the water and be driven under again by the wasps.

They survived it but I'm sure they leave sleeping snakes sleeping now.

Fleas

Can make your legs look like they've been sprinkled with black pepper when you step into the part of the flower bed where your dog sleeps. They can run a grown man out of his own backyard. These pests are very agile, elusive, hopping from one part of your body to the other, sometimes biting as they go, escaping from your fingertips before you can crush 'em, when you finally manage to catch one. The bite they inflict is not real painful but the long lasting itch that follows is a real nuisance.

Fire Ants

Hundreds of the vicious ants can have crawled up to your knees unnoticed, especially in the dark when you are standing in the middle of their bed. Waiting to all start biting at once when you start trying to remove them by stamping your feet and beating 'em off your legs with your hands, then stinging your hands and marching up your arms. I have found that jumping in the nearest creek or pond is the quickest way to remove them. Each ant bite leaves a painful red whelp that tends to get a little pus head on it the next day. The pesky fire ant has been blamed for the demise of the quail populations, able to kill the baby quail when they try to dust themselves in the edge of the ant bed with only two or three bites.

We have quite a few more insects that can hurt you like Cow-Killer ants, Thousand Leggers, certain centipedes and caterpillars but the ones I've mentioned earlier seem to be the most common and aggressive.

I've been taught, and truly believe, that everything made by our Creator has it's place and serves a purpose. Evidently the Gulf coastline is the biting insects place cause you can't get rid of 'em no matter what you do. As to the insect's purpose: I believe it is to fuel the coastal real-estate market cause the Yankees come down in the winter and buy their places on the marsh, enjoying the outdoors and no snow. Then they move down here in the summer, get chewed, gnawed and ravaged by our bugs, immediately re-listing their dream home and moving far inland.

The Yankees won't quit coming and the bugs won't quit biting.

Perpetual Motion.

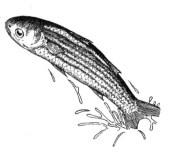

Redneck Physical Therapy

Little Ralph was a country-boy. Born and raised in the south, fishing and hunting his whole life. He was a football player in high school and college, a line-backer, a big strong guy.

He was still big and strong, but a lot more bigger than stronger, cause he'd put on quite a beer belly in the fifteen or twenty years since he had played ball in · college.

And that beer belly was causing Little Ralph back problems. Least that's what they told 'em at the doctor's office. They told 'em to cut down on his beer and bar-b-que, his Vienna sausage, sardines and saltines. They also recommended that he see a chiropractor, maybe that could help, but he really needed to lose weight, that was the problem.

Little Ralph decides he's going to try the chiropractor right away. He's got to have some relief from the pressure on his back and he's not about to quit drinking and eating what he wants.

He goes and sits in the nearest chiropractor's office till he can be seen by the doctor. They finally call 'em back and strap 'em to a table and raise it to where Little Ralph is almost upside down.

Instant unbelievable relief.

Little Ralph likes this, he can feel his bones crackling a little as they get put in place, he can feel the weight and pressure of that forty pound beer-belly come off his back.

This is the kind of treatment I need every once in a while, Little Ralph's thinking, as he pays his $50.00 to the receptionist. He's feeling better than he has in a long time.

And he goes back to work, and back to hunting and

fishing and football season partying, gaining a few more pounds.

And back he goes to the chiropractor at $50.00 a clip, and back again, but it feels so good to get that relief. Little Ralph is shelling out that fifty bucks at least once a week, sometimes twice.

It's a week-day afternoon and Little Ralph is out at the pole-barn behind his house, looking for his chainsaw to cut some firewood. He's moaning and groaning every time he bends over to move something, his back is hurting and he's thinking about getting a treatment and how expensive and inconvenient it is to go to town and have it done.

All of a sudden Little Ralph spies a set of old snow skis leaning against the wall, a pair he used in Colorado ten or fifteen years ago when he weighed about 220 instead of the 270 he weighed now.

An idea blossoms and grows in his head.

He goes immediately to work.

He gets his skill saw and cuts both snow skis off just ahead and behind the place where you clamp your boots on to the skis.

He finds a heavy piece of lumber about two-foot square, drills a hole in the center of it and secures a one-inch eye bolt to it.

On the opposite side that the eye bolt is sticking out of, Little Ralph takes the boot-clamp-on part of the skis, and drills and bolts both of them to the board.

That part of the equipment is ready to go as Little Ralph has tried on the device, clamping on his laced-up Redwing boots to make sure the fit is snug.

Now Little Ralph is an avid deer hunter and to be a deer hunter you have to have a four-wheel drive pick-up truck. And that pick-up truck has got to have a winch on the front to pull it out of bog-holes. No need to go in the woods without it.

That truck and winch are very important parts in

Little Ralph's scheme.

As is the perfect limb on one of the giant oak trees growing in Little Ralph's backyard.

He's studying those now, head sticking out of the window of his pick-up, looking up at the limbs of those oaks, placing the front of his truck in perfect position underneath a foot-thick oak limb, protruding out almost perpendicular about twelve feet off the ground.

Now Little Ralph pulls about thirty feet of steel cable off the spool of the winch. He grabs the end of the cable, where the big steel hook is, and throws it over that big oak limb, taking up the slack in the cable to where the hook is barely touching the ground.

The winch on Little Ralph's truck is equipped with a push button switch, that is attached to the winch by a curly-cued cord, much like telephones used to come with. He's got the control switch stretched out to where he can reach it.

Ralph sits down on the ground by where the hook and the cable is dangling from the limb. He's clamping on his sawed-off snow skis that are bolted to the board.

He attaches the hook on the end of the cable to the eye bolt through the board.

Now he reaches for the control switch to the winch and takes it in his hand. He is laying flat on his back with his toes pointed up, punching the button on the switch off and on, off and on and his feet slowly lift off the ground with each press. He presses the button till his butt clears the ground and only his shoulders are touching.

Instant relief to his aching back.

Victory is mine, Little Ralph's thinking as he raises his entire body into a vertical up-side-down position by taking up more cable on the winch, his head clearing mother earth by an inch.

Little Ralph is in ecstasy.

All the pressure is gone off his back, his legs and

spine are getting a good stretch-out. It feels even better than the fifty-dollar-a-pop treatment at the clinic.

Little Ralph's got his eyes closed, arms hanging limp to the ground, the winch control button in his hand.

He opens his eyes and notices there's a kink in the curly-cued cord that runs the control switch to the winch on the front bumper of his truck. We've all had phone cords get kinked and wadded up and had to flip and twirl the cord to get it out.

Little Ralph kinda flips the cord over itself to straighten it out, and watches as the remote control cord unplugs itself from the winch and falls to the ground.

Now he can't let himself down.

And now he's noticing that his big beer-belly is pressing on his lungs and guts, and that all his blood is starting to run to his head cause his heart wasn't designed to pump up-side down for long periods of time.

He's helpless and in trouble, suspended wrong-side-up by a cable thrown over an oak limb, looking like a giant opossum hanging by a long grey tail.

He starts to yell for Becky, his wife, who's in the house cooking supper.

And at first the yells are long and loud and Becky hears 'em.

But she's used to Ralph yelling cause he yells for her all the time and usually it's because he can't find a tool or a gun or a rod or his truck keys and he stops yelling as soon as he finds what he was looking for.

The yelling stops in a minute or so and she finishes setting the table, thinking Little Ralph's found what was lost.

Little Ralph is still yelling, but not much sound is coming out. All that blood that's drained to his head and all that beer-gut that's squashing his heart and lungs has got Little Ralph barely squeaking out sounds. He is real red in the face.

Becky's thru cooking dinner and has all the groceries

on the table.

She hollers out the door for Little Ralph and there is no reply.

She yells again.

No answer.

She looks toward the pole-barn and sees a sight she just can't quite figure out. It looks like a man hanging upside-down from a cable thrown over a big oak limb and tied off to a pick-up truck.

She runs down to find Little Ralph, spitting and a sputtering, face redder than an over-ripe tomato, pointing and gesturing toward the winch on his truck, still holding the winch control button in his hand.

Becky doesn't know anything about remote controls, or truck winches. All she knows is her husband's head is about to explode, his eyes are popping out and he can't hardly speak or breathe.

She runs to the house and calls 911.

Lucky for them the "good ole boys" on the emergency response unit get there in time and they know all about truck winches, cause they all got 'em too. The EMT just plugs the remote cord back in the winch control, pushes the reverse button and lowers Little Ralph back down to the ground.

They console Little Ralph's wife, give Little Ralph some oxygen, all the time trying not to snicker and laugh at the crazy situation they had just responded to.

Little Ralph's wheezing and sputtering, Becky's crying and pampering, trying to get an explanation out of her husband as to why and what.

I guess Little Ralph explained it to her when he could talk again.

I'm sure he probably started his trips back to the chiropractor again.

But he may have just worked the "kinks" out of his Redneck physical therapy session and continued to treat himself.

Who knows about Little Ralph.

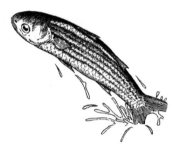

Goose Creek, December 26, 2002

Never have fully understood what-creek-was-what, by name, in "Goose Creek".

But what I call "Goose Creek", is actually the mouth of a small short river, formed by two spring-fed creeks that run together amid a complex series of oyster-bars and marsh-grass islands. With deep holes in the bends of the creeks and those deep holes scattered with rock, and the rocks guarded by fish, mostly mullet, sometimes trout and reds.

Sometimes big gators guard those rocks - and that's another story, but when the weather gets real cold and the water gets low, an airboat tide, you can just about bank on the dapper mullet getting thick around the rocks in those muddy dark holes.

That's what I counted on the day we opened the restaurant back up and needed fish to serve.

Tide low at a quarter to one in the afternoon.

You need an hour or so for the incoming tide to slack the flow of the fresh water running to the gulf, so we're in no hurry. The Nor-easter that's pushing twenty knots of wind is blowing the bay dry, making the pools we want to fish in landlocked and that bunches the fish even tighter, which is what we need with just two, eighty-foot nets to catch 'em with.

But that airboat's the ticket, the only machine we could have to do the job, like we need to do it.

Fast, efficient, the shallower the water the better it runs, even picking up speed on mud or wet grass-flat.

Three hundred and fifty cubic inch GM motor.

Three hundred and thirty horsepower with a six-bladed carbon fiber propeller mounted on an eighteen-foot, heavy gauge aluminum rectangle of a boat, custom designed to strike a net off the front, into those rocky pools.

We blow around Oyster Bay and Shell Point at about forty, turning north past Live Oak Island looking at the mouth of Goose Creek about two miles away.

The tide's got the water out five-hundred yards from the shore line.

I'm already picturing the land-locked pool I'm checking out first, knowing it's loaded with mullet, guiding the boat around the first sets of oyster bars, not even looking for fish yet.

I back off the throttle, slowing down as we slide across two hundred yards of black mud to my targeted pool.

The water is dark as coffee from all the rain and you can't see down in it to tell if there's any fish packed-up, laying on the bottom.

I make two lazy circles around the pool, watching for any kind of a whirl or motion in the center.

There's a couple swirls, then a single fish darts across the center and then another one jumps my mud-wake and I know what's fixing to happen.

I'm fixing to pitch this five pound sash-weight I've got in my hand, over-board, and that sash-weight, (called the staff from the old days of paddle boat fishing), is attached by rope to the end of my little-biddy net coiled on the bow of the airboat.

I'm also fixing to stand that airboat on it's nose, in as hard a turn as it will do, to try and make a complete closed circle around where I think the fish are.

Believe me, it's a trick to close the circle with only a hundred and sixty total feet of net, to put overboard, but I manage this time and the circle explodes with fish. Fish jumping the net, fish jumping on the net table, fish foaming up the corkline, sinking it in some places so many are in it.

We idle up to the end of the net and grab it, each of

us taking either the lead line or the float line trying to keep a bag or bend in the netting cause the fish are just laying up in it, not really caught or gilled just fighting the webbing trying to get out.

We have to trip the net and the fish together on the boat in a quick orderly fashion, not trying to clear the net as we take it up cause all the rest of the fish will work their way out if we wait.

Over half of 'em fall out any way, from these sorry little nets we have to use.

We got a hundred, maybe a hundred and twenty five pounds of mullet, three big trout that we have to throw back, illegal for us to keep, and one fifteen pound redfish that tore my net all to pieces and we have to throw him back too.

But we've got what we need for a day or two and we haven't been gone an hour.

We'll just leave all the rest of these fish that are bunched up in these holes till we need more for the restaurant.

The fish stay a lot fresher stored over here in Goose Creek, till we need more. They stay fresh forever as a matter of fact, swimming free and being fattened and fed by old Mother Nature.

From December to March we just need a low-low tide, an airboat and we can count on catching 'em like you count on getting milk at the grocery store.

Sunny Days

We built a house by the sea.

The first night we spent there we lay on a mattress with our little boys and picked out animals from the grain in the wood paneling by lantern light. We cooked on a Coleman stove, and bathed in water spewing from our new well in the back yard.

Soon after, we got real appliances and bathtubs and pictures for the walls. Furniture was plucked from here and there and painted and slip covered and comfy.

Every time we visited the house we picked flowers from around, and shells from the shore. We opened the windows and doors so that the sea breeze blew through and lifted the filmy curtains from the bedroom windows.

We spent our days outside the house. We floated on rafts, lay on blankets, scurried up dunes. We caught crabs, netted fish, chased sting rays. We lay flat on the sand and watched puffer belly clouds float through the sky.

We welcomed friends and family to visit our house. We shared our rockers and sheets and pantry with brothers and sisters, parents, schoolmates, aunts and uncles, cousins, and total strangers. Neighbors always came to dinner; most with fine beach houses and boats and some with planes. But none had the bounty of fish and crabs that we did. None had more beautiful children than we did with skin tanned by the sun and hair streaked gold by the sun. None had a better view of the diamond strewn bay. None saw more clearly the sunsets that looked like God had dropped a piece of heaven right outside our door.

Tides come and go, and in time our footprints are erased. We no longer have the house by the sea. But the laughter, the sunshine and love we found there is forever ours.

We found a house in a forest in the woods.

- Anonymous

What a Great Place to Be

Man it's nice standing here on the dock.

Watching the wind blow the clouds by the full moon, the clouds getting thicker and darker as they slide under the moon. The open spaces between the clouds getting smaller and tighter as the weather thickens up and gets heavier.

The cold front is getting closer, sucking all the Gulf's warmth and moisture into it.

Making the violent weather. The weather on the edge of the cold-dry, warm-wet collision of opposing forces of nature, that makes all us men bow down and heed this weather change.

I'm watching this weather shape up while I'm standing on dry ground, fifty yards from a shower with hot water and a bed that doesn't move.

A dry place.

A warm place.

A place with no fear for your life, boat and equipment.

"Let it blow and rain, I've put my time in," I think to myself.

Then I think of all the boats still working out there.

The bow rising and falling. The water dripping through the bow cap scuttle hole. The blankets all damp from days of salt moisture in the air and wet fishy clothes, trying to sleep in 'em.

Trying to sleep and relax and not being too successful. Waves slamming the bow, spray slapping the windshield like rain, wind howling thru the rigging, water constantly dripping and sloshing on the back deck and in the bilge.

And if we're real lucky the weather won't get any

worse and we'll have the opportunity to try and fish in this mess tomorrow.

Oh what dry clothes, a still bed, a warm shower and hot food are worth. You can't appreciate it for its full value if you haven't had it regular.

I'm glad I'm on the hill.

But for some crazy reason I still miss it - just a little bit.

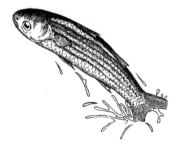